The First 350 Years of the
Harvard University Library

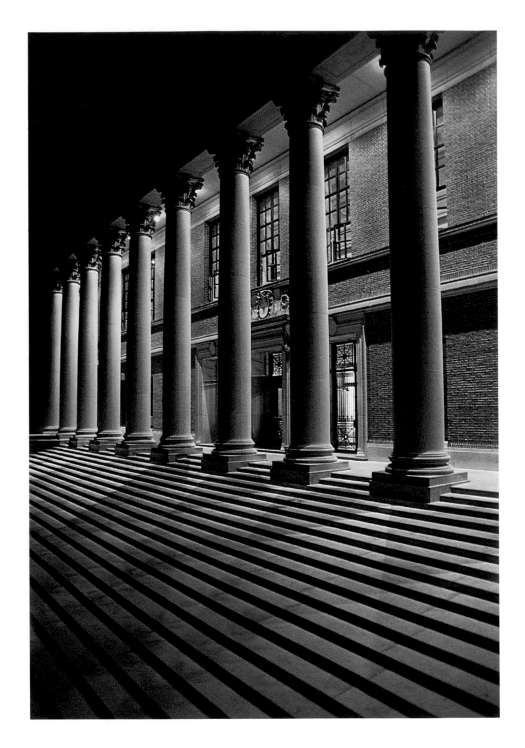

The Harry Elkins Widener Memorial Library

The First 350 Years of the Harvard University Library

Description of an Exhibition

by

Kenneth E. Carpenter

Harvard University Library

CAMBRIDGE · MASSACHUSETTS

1986

Foreword

The Harvard University Library is one of the world's great conservators of the written word, but the institution itself has not been conservative. Its history is not just a story of oaks from acorns. John Harvard's bequest, which created the first library in the English colonies, did not preordain the library's present contribution to learning. That has come about because generation after generation of men (and since 1859, women) have changed the library. Numerous and diverse individuals — young graduates who were "library keepers," modern professionals, Harvard faculty, loyal Harvard alumni, lovers of learning throughout the world, booksellers, Harvard presidents, and more recently foundation executives and government officials — have fostered, along with growth, creative change in response to problems and opportunities. Growth and change have gone together.

Size has been a major incentive to innovation and creative response. But today, the pressures on the Library stem from much else besides size, and Harvard's library problems and opportunities are shared by libraries throughout the world. Effective responses will sometimes demand joint efforts fostered by national organizations or governmental bodies. In other instances, the common good may be well served by an individual librarian who perceives a possibility for creative change and acts on it. But whatever the source of initiatives and whatever their demands, I, like my predecessors, believe that the Harvard Library must participate in solving its generation's library and information problems.

This book illustrates the innovative and influential changes that have taken place in the Harvard Library, from the development of card catalogs and pioneering efforts to foster their use, through new paths in collecting and buildings planned for new purposes, down to the development today of advanced computer programs for library functions. It is my belief that the forces that made possible both growth and change are still at work in the University today. As the Library begins its second 350 years, my charge is that it contribute to scholarship through continuing to form great collections and through continuing to deal creatively with this generation's library problems and opportunities.

DEREK BOK
President, Harvard University

Preface

This work, which catalogs an exhibition prepared in connection with the celebration of the 350th anniversary of Harvard University, is, I believe, much more than an exhibition catalog. The entries in this publication, richly illustrated and fully annotated by Kenneth E. Carpenter, trace the history of the Harvard University Library. One can follow the development of the Harvard Library from the initial bequest by John Harvard of about 400 volumes to its present state as the largest university library (and the largest non-public library) in the world, with some 11 million volumes and countless other items, from photographs, to data tapes, to video cassettes. And one can follow the evolution of the means to catalog, store, and retrieve these materials.

The massiveness of the Harvard collection and the determination of the Library to maintain a strong collection in almost all fields has forced it to face complex issues of storage and cataloging. In tackling them, the Library has often developed innovative ways of handling library materials. This book illustrates such innovations, ranging from catalog cards to self-supporting library stacks; innovations that are now common in libraries. Catalog cards have, of course, in turn become obsolete, and one can see represented here stages in the development of the newer computer-based catalogs now being used at Harvard.

This book is a history of the Harvard Library and that makes it, as well, a history of Harvard University. Ever since the University took the name of its first library donor, it has grown with and around the Library. The commitment of Harvard College to fine undergraduate education is paralleled by the development of a series of undergraduate libraries: from the intimate House libraries to Lamont, Hilles, and Cabot. The commitment of the University to a role of world leadership in scholarship parallels and depends upon the growth of the research collections in the flagship Widener Library and in the multitude of specialized libraries. And, as modern scholarship changes and takes on new approaches that require access to electronic information networks, Harvard scholars shape the newer services provided by the University Library system.

The history of the Harvard Library may also be seen as a history of culture and of scholarship. Libraries record the scholarship and culture of the day. What they collect — whether the papers of New England's great authors in the Houghton Library, or journals in science departmental libraries, or materials in formerly esoteric languages by specialized departments — reflects the society's culture and values. Libraries also contribute to the culture and the scholarship of the next day as the works they contain are read, revised, and superseded by new scholarship. The ways in which they further that process — whether by keeping longer hours, putting books on reserve, providing reference services, microfilming rare or fragile volumes, or helping users search computerized databases — also reflect society's needs and values.

This volume is a record of that great, innovative record-keeping and record-disseminating institution.

SIDNEY VERBA
Carl H. Pforzheimer University Professor and
Director of the University Library

Introduction

A book or exhibition based on the history of the Harvard Library cannot avoid expressing a sense of grandeur about the Library, even a feeling of awe over its size and richness. Such a feeling does exist about a great library, even among those who daily work in it. To enter the Widener stacks on 4 East and walk past rows and rows of American history to 4 West, and then to go down the stairs to level D, past the record of culture after culture, in order to find a book on Scandinavia or on Swiss history — that is an emotional as well as physical journey. In the Widener classification scheme used until the adoption of the Library of Congress classification in 1976, books are classified much more by culture than by subject; and anyone who is motivated by a desire to enter into other cultures finds Widener a place of endless possibilities.

For a Harvard librarian to give a tour of the University is another kind of emotional journey, for perhaps in no other community are books so omnipresent. In the course of the tour one might leave the Yard and proceed as follows: "There's the Cabot Science Library which was especially built for undergraduates but also has rows and rows of old scientific and technical publications in the basement; though few undergraduates need them, they still have all kinds of uses for scholars. Recently, someone researched in them the ways in which fear of fire and the resulting insurance regulations have shaped American buildings and communities. The Library, you know, almost never throws anything out." Going on to Divinity Avenue, one could point out to the visitor that "on your right is the largest university collection on East Asia; its Tibetan scrolls, wrapped in orange cloth, are an impressive sight. The Tozzer Library of Anthropology over there has an extraordinary index of anthropological articles, which it began early in this century; beyond Tozzer, in that building, is the Gray Herbarium library and other botanical libraries, and behind them is the great Divinity School Library, whose early books, thanks to years of steady conservation work, must be one of the finest looking collections anywhere." Turning left, one might point out the existence of libraries in the University Museum: the Museum of Comparative Zoology Library and the Geological Sciences Library. "Those are not just a few books in a room; the MCZ is approaching 250,000 volumes. Beyond is the largest university music library, and in Langdell Hall over there is the world's greatest legal library. Actually its collections are housed in several of the buildings you can see." Of course, only a long tour could cover all those in the Boston area, such as the world's largest collection of business literature and the Countway Library of Medicine, which is the country's second largest medical library. Extended journeys would be required to visit other Harvard libraries in such locations as Washington, D.C., or Florence, Italy.

One could point out that within the large and individually distinguished libraries are many special collections of high quality. Within Widener, for instance, is Harry Nelson Gay's collection on nineteenth-century Italy, which was the work of a Harvard graduate resident in Italy who spent a lifetime collecting and studying the Risorgimento movement. The Classics collection is superb, thanks to on-going purchases in the past but also to gifts of special collections, such as Professor Morris Hickey Morgan's Persius collection, or Professor John W. White's of Aristophanes. Philosophy was long selected by Benjamin Rand, the compiler of an exhaustive bibliography, and among the Harvard philosophers whose libraries are here are Hugo Münsterberg, Josiah Royce, and William James. Author after author is represented by collections that were lovingly formed. To name only two: the Dante Collection, which was enriched by the great Harvard scholar Charles Eliot Norton; or the Cervantes Collection, formed by Carl T. Keller. (W. A. Jackson was able to purchase the great gap, the first edition of Don Quixote, when Keller lay dying — and to inform him of the acquisition.) Along with discussing these in this catalog, one could have pointed out that the walls of the Houghton exhibition room are lined with books printed before 1501. Or one might have emphasized the numerous special collections in faculty libraries, perhaps the archival records being preserved in the Countway Library of Medicine, or the pre-1850 business and economic literature in the Kress Library at the Business School; it never ceases to amaze that a school devoted to teaching the latest in business administration should also cherish early books.

Along with emphasizing special collections that are notable for their completeness and the rarity of the material in them, this book could have focused on individual items, ranging from manuscripts in this country's largest collection of medieval and Renaissance manuscripts, to first editions of great authors and thinkers.

This catalog does convey an impression of the size of the collections, their diversity, and their strength, but its emphasis is somewhat different. It tries to further understanding of how the Library came to have such strength and diversity in collections, how librarians and others have faced the task of cataloging the collections, housing and preserving them, and helping students and scholars use them.

Much more than a celebration of grandeur, this catalog is also a history of the problems and opportunities that individuals, often quirky individuals, faced, or, in some cases, failed to perceive. Librarians and others often acted with great wisdom to shape the Library; in other instances chance played a major role. In a sense the absence of central control in the Library and the University has even fostered chance. It has encouraged the entrepreneurial building of collections by librarians, and by others as well. It has enabled books to be widely dispersed, which removes any single factor as a determinant of policy.

There is something about the life of this institution that is very much like the life of an individual. Seeming failures sometimes led to later developments; Croswell's catalog of the 1810s, made in part by pasting slips on sheets, was never completed, but his idea of slips seems to have led to a card catalog, the first in the country. Small steps occasionally — and sometimes accidentally — formed the basis for major new directions: the Corporation's delegation of book selection to a committee — and the later inclusion on it of faculty members — established a mechanism that subsequently permitted book selection on a large scale. (Small steps also sometimes exerted a long-lasting influence for the worse, such as Winsor's setting up a special room for Radcliffe students.) At times something most devoutly wanted, above all a new building to replace Gore Hall, would probably have been unfortunate if obtained when first needed.

This catalog does not try to depict the Library's evolution as one purposeful accomplishment after another. There were many, and, indeed, the history of the institution is filled with innovative responses to problems and individuals who creatively seized opportunities. In numerous instances, however, people could not break away from preconceptions derived from the past. It seems that we today also find our options shaped by the past and that one of the desirable tasks for those who work in an institution is to understand its past. In doing so, one does not transcend the past. Decentralization, for instance, is a fact of the Harvard Library environment, for better and for worse. But understanding the Library's history is one means by which the individuals who work in it today can more effectively overcome those factors that inhibit productive change and enhance those that foster creativity in the institution. And perhaps those who interact with the Library, whether Harvard administrators, librarians elsewhere, foundation executives, or private donors, can more effectively accomplish their goals, if they are more conscious of the factors that have historically been at work in the Library.

It is hoped that Harvard librarians and those who are concerned with the Library in one capacity or another will find that this publication fosters understanding as we set out on the next segment of the Library's history. The story here is certainly not complete. For instance, it is not noted that Coolidge reconstructed the Harvard catalog as well as expanded the collections. This publication is more, though, than an assortment of disparate entries, and readers who wish to pursue a particular topic will find that the entries, though separated, can be brought together by using the index, which has topical references as well as references to names and libraries.

It is also hoped that readers will include those who are not intimately connected with libraries, for technical language has been avoided and illustrations have been chosen with the general reader in mind.

Acknowledgements

Many have contributed to this exhibition in various ways. Harley Holden, Curator of the University Archives, and the staff of the Archives, gave me unusual access to the collections and answered a host of questions. Clark Elliott informed me that an exhibition had been commissioned and mounted by a student, Kevin L. Cope, in 1979 and that the record existed; I have greatly benefited from that work. It soon turned out when I read what had been written on the Library that my "discoveries" had often been made before. The very first issue of the *Harvard Library Bulletin* in 1947 had an article by Keyes D. Metcalf on "The Undergraduate and the Harvard Library, 1765–1877." Robert W. Lovett wrote a continuation, and numerous other articles in the HLB have been relied upon. In 1939 the Library had published Clarence E. Walton's *The Three-Hundredth Anniversary of the Harvard College Library*, a well written pamphlet, which has been of great help. William Bentinck-Smith's *Building a Great Library: The Coolidge Years at Harvard* (1976) is a thoroughly researched and beautifully written book. Among other books and articles on the history of libraries in the United States, I have profited above all from *The University Library in the United States: Its Origins and Development* (1981), by Arthur T. Hamlin, a Harvard graduate and former Harvard librarian. That this exhibition does not place the history of the Harvard Library more in the context of library developments elsewhere is only partially a reflection of the lack of full-length histories for other major university libraries of the East Coast.

Susanna Kaysen improved the prose, as did numerous other individuals who also saved me from a variety of pitfalls: Charles Berlin, Lawrence Dowler, Alan Erickson, G. Edward Evans, Dale Flecker, Joan Nordell, and especially Edwin E. Williams. Numerous librarians have read the sections that particularly concern their areas of the

1638

The College is Named
for a Donor of Books

Sixteen years after the Pilgrims landed at Plymouth, the settlers established a college in Cambridge. It was a struggling institution, with, it appears, some books, though few. Two years later, in 1638, John Harvard, a graduate of Emmanuel College, Cambridge, who had come to Charlestown in 1637, died and left all his books and half his estate to the unnamed College. Some six months later the Great and General Court of the Massachusetts Bay Colony ordered "that the colledge agreed vpon formerly to bee built at Cambridg shalbee called Harvard Colledge." John Harvard's gift was by far the largest that the College had yet received, and not until 1678 did Harvard College receive a larger gift of books.

John Harvard's library contained some 329 titles representing about 400 volumes. John Downame's *Christian Warfare* (1633/34), one of only 404 volumes to have survived the disastrous fire of 1764, is almost certainly the copy bequeathed by John Harvard. It, like a large number of the other books saved, was out — and overdue.

The sole surviving book from John Harvard's library.

1642

John Harvard's Library Is Housed in Old College

The first structure erected for academic purposes was begun in 1638 and finished in 1642. In this College, thought by some "to be too gorgeous for a Wilderness," the "good Library" was housed on the second floor at the east end. No contemporary description of the library room exists. Five of the original Overseers were, however, graduates of Trinity College in Cambridge, and it would be strange if its library had not served as a pattern. A row of lecterns with shelves below the desks and with half-lecterns on each end-wall would have provided more shelving than was initially required. The benches could later have been replaced by more lecterns, and the space would have been sufficient for all the books ever needing to be housed in Old College.

The Library was located in a room on the second floor. From this angle, the room was at the rear left.

Above: The Library as it probably looked in Old College; *below:* Plan of the second floor of Old College.

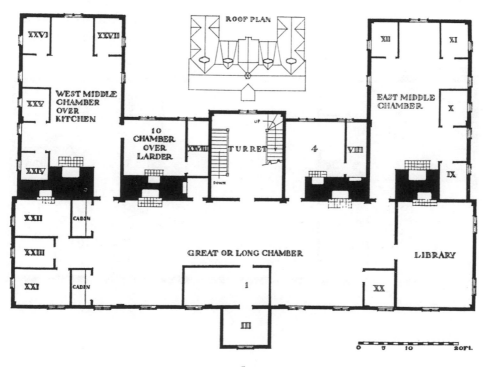

5

The Library Moves to
New College

The original College building required such expensive repairs because of its poor construction that in 1671 it was decided to to build a replacement. During the summer of 1677 the library could be moved to the new building, two years before the old was reported to have "fallen doune, a part of it." Daniel Gookin, the third Librarian, received £2.10.6 for doing the moving. In the new hall the Library occupied the central space on the second floor, in a room about 30-by-40-feet. In the Library the tops of the lecterns were probably sawed off and the shelves extended toward the ceiling.

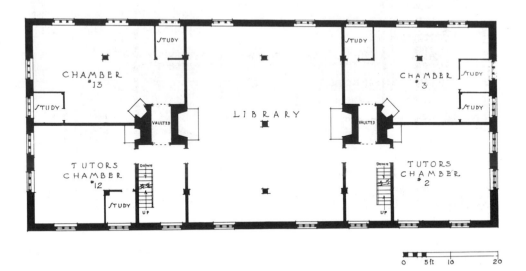

Above: A detail from a 1726 print, which depicts New College; *left*: This plan of the second floor of New College shows the Library in the center room.

Harvard Publishes a Library Catalog

Harvard published in 1723 the first library catalog in what is now the United States. It was compiled by the Librarian Joshua Gee, for £20 extra compensation. B. Green, whose name appears in the imprint, set the type, but Samuel Gerrish was the printer. He printed 400 copies, 300 for Harvard, and 100 on his account.

The catalog of 3,100 titles was not published primarily to disseminate information. Its main goal was to stimulate gifts. A catalog was first suggested by Daniel Neal in a letter to President Leverett on 6 August 1720. Neal was pastor of a congregation of Dissenters in London and had encouraged Thomas Hollis and others to make gifts to the College. Hollis seconded the suggestion.

After printing, 100 copies of the catalog were sent to England. By 8 May 1724 Hollis was able to report that he had distributed 38 copies. He was sufficiently pleased with their effect to request a supplement on 6 January 1724/25. He did, however, have complaints about the catalog. The books were arranged by format: folio, quarto, octavo, and smaller. In compiling the catalog, Gee probably began with blank pages on which he wrote each letter of the alphabet. Then, beginning with the folios, he recorded each book, according to its author (or title, if anonymous), on its proper page. He then did the same for quartos, and so on. Hollis did not complain that the user had to look in four alphabetical series. What he regretted was that "all books of One Author, of same size" did not stand together, for in each series authors' names were grouped by letter but not alphabetized further.

Since each entry in Gee's catalog includes the shelfmark, it is apparent that within each size the Library's books were arranged by subject. At the beginning of the classification were Bibles.

CATALOGUS
LIBRORUM
BIBLIOTHECÆ
Collegij Harvardini

Quod est

CANTABRIGIÆ
IN
Nova Anglia.

BOSTONI NOV-ANGLORUM:
Typis *B. Green,* Academiæ Typographi. MDCCXXIII.

The 1723 catalog.
Supplements were published in 1725 and 1735.

9

Benjamin Franklin
Proposes a Book Fund

In 1755 Benjamin Franklin proposed the novel idea that the College seek subscriptions to a fund for books, whose annual income would be "sufficient to procure the best new Books published in each year." He backed up the idea by entering his own name on the form for subscribers.

Franklin's name is alone on the subscription sheet, and his order that the College be paid 4 pistoles remained uncashed — signs that the College authorities may have recognized the implications of Franklin's proposal. A fund for steady acquisitions would have created pressures for major changes in the Library.

The "library keeper," as the librarian was then called, was exactly that. He delivered the books that users wanted, recorded the borrowings, and then checked that the books had been returned. Usually a recent graduate of the College, he was not expected to do more. The College handled a major task, such as creating a new catalog, by appropriating funds for special work, which was done by someone other than the library keeper, or by him for additional compensation. Books were then, for the most part, added by gift, not purchase.

Although the College could muster resources and make decisions about specific tasks, even large ones, the Library was not seen as an institution requiring regular nourishment and support. Not until a century later, in 1857, did the College appeal for support to buy "the best new books," and not until a couple of decades after that did there begin to be adequate support in the form of endowed funds rather than gifts for current use.

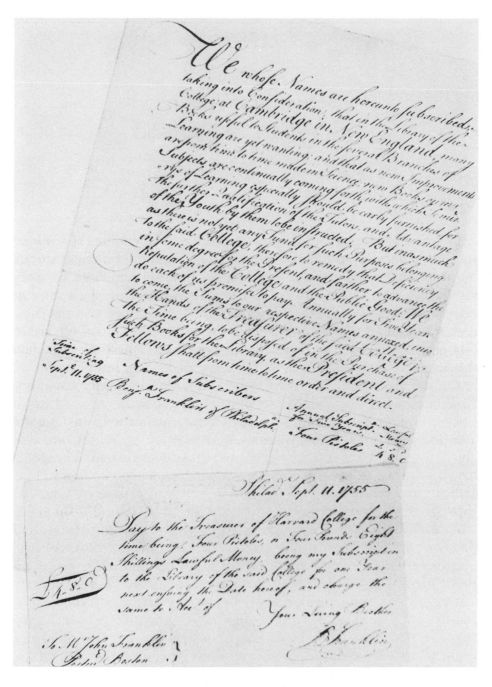

The subscription form for Franklin's proposed fund and his order for payment. Subscribers to funds did in fact what the Latin roots of the word suggest; they wrote their names under. See p. 81 for an example of a subscription book from the following century.

1764

The Library Burns

"Last night Harvard College, suffered the most ruinous loss it ever met with since its foundation. In the middle of a very tempestuous night, a severe cold storm of snow attended with high wind, we were awaked by the alarm of fire." So began the *Account of the Fire at Harvard-College*, the fire that destroyed the largest library in the colonies. Of about 5,000 volumes, only 404 survived. They were either out on loan or, though received by the Library, had not yet been unpacked.

On the morning of 25 January the Harvard community could not have known that its "ruinous loss" would soon be made good by so generous an outpouring of gifts that by Commencement in 1766 the Library would total 4,350 volumes.

An Account of the Fire at *Harvard-College*,

in *Cambridge* ; with the Loss suſtained thereby.

CAMBRIDGE, Jan. 25. 1764.

LAST night HARVARD COLLEGE, ſuffered the moſt ruinous loſs it ever met with ſince its foundation. In the middle of a very tempeſtuous night, a ſevere cold ſtorm of ſnow attended with high wind, we were awaked by the alarm of fire. *Harvard*-Hall, the only one of our ancient buildings which ſtill remained,* and the repoſitory of our moſt valuable treaſures, the public LIBRARY and Philoſophical APPARATUS, was ſeen in flames. As it was a time of vacation, in which the ſtudents were all diſperſed, not a ſingle perſon was left in any of the Colleges, except two or three in that part of *Maſſachuſetts* moſt diſtant from *Harvard*, where the fire could not be perceived till the whole ſurrounding air began to be illuminated by it : When it was diſcovered from the town, it had riſen to a degree of violence that defied all oppoſition. It is conjectured to have begun in a beam under the hearth in the library, where a fire had been kept for the uſe of the General Court, now reſiding and ſitting here, by reaſon of the Small-Pox at Boſton : from thence it burſt out into the Library. The books eaſily ſubmitted to the fury of the flame, which with a rapid and irreſiſtable progreſs made its way into the Apparatus-Chamber, and ſpread thro' the whole building. In a very ſhort time, this venerable Monument of the Piety of our Anceſtors was turn'd into an heap of ruins. The other Colleges, *Stoughton*-Hall and *Maſſachuſetts*-Hall, were in the utmoſt hazard of ſharing the ſame fate. The wind driving the flaming cinders directly upon their roofs, they blazed out ſeveral times in different places ; nor could they have been ſaved by all the help the Town could afford, had it not been for the aſſiſtance of the Gentlemen of the General Court, among whom his Excellency the Governor was very active ; who, notwithſtanding the extreme rigor of the ſeaſon, exerted themſelves in ſupplying the town Engine with water, which they were obliged to fetch at laſt from a diſtance, two of the College pumps being then rendered uſeleſs. Even the new and beautiful *Hollis*-Hall, though it was on the windward ſide, hardly eſcaped. It ſtood ſo near to *Harvard*, that the flames actually ſeized it and, if they had not been immediately ſuppreſſed, muſt have carried it.

But by the Bleſſing of God on the vigorous efforts of the aſſiſtants, the ruin was confined to *Harvard*-Hall ; and there, beſides the deſtruction of the private property of thoſe who had chambers in it, the public loſs is very great ; perhaps, irreparable. The Library and the Apparatus, which for many years had been growing, and were now judged to be the beſt furniſhed in America, are annihilated. But to give the public a more diſtinct idea of the loſs, we ſhall exhibit a ſummary view of the general contents of each, as far as we can, on a ſudden, recollect them.

Of the LIBRARY.

IT contained—The Holy Scriptures in almoſt all languages, with the moſt valuable Expoſitors and Commentators, ancient and modern :—The whole Library of the late learned Dr. Lightfoot, which at his death lie bequeathed to this College, and contained the Targums, Talmuds, Rabbins, Polyglot, and other valuable tracts relative to oriental literature, which is taught here : The library of the late eminent Dr. Theophilus Gale : —

* *Harvard*-Hall, 42 feet broad, 97 long, and four ſtories high, was founded A. D. 1672.

—All the Fathers, Greek and Latin, in their beſt editions. — A great number of tracts in defence of revealed religion, wrote by the moſt maſterly hands, in the laſt and preſent century :— Sermons of the moſt celebrated Engliſh divines, both of the eſtabliſhed national church and proteſtant diſſenters :—Tracts upon all the branches of polemic divinity :—The donation of the venerable Society for propagating the Goſpel in foreign parts, conſiſting of a great many volumes of tracts againſt Popery, publiſhed in the Reigns of Charles II. and James II. the Boylean lectures, and other the moſt eſteemed Engliſh ſermons :—A valuable collection of modern theological treatiſes, preſented by the Right Rev. Dr. Sherlock, late Lord Biſhop of London, the Rev. Dr. Hales, F. R. S. and Dr. Wilſon of London :—A vaſt number of philological tracts, containing the rudiments of almoſt all languages, ancient and modern :—The Hebrew, Greek and Roman antiquities.—The Greek and Roman Claſſics, preſented by the late excellent and catholic-ſpirited Biſhop Berkeley ; moſt of them the beſt editions :—A large Collection of Hiſtory and biographical tracts, ancient and modern.—Diſſertations on various Political ſubjects —The Tranſactions of the Royal Society, Academy of Sciences in France, Acta Eruditorum, Miſcellanea curioſa, the works of Boyle and Newton, with a great variety of other mathematical and philoſophical treatiſes.—A collection of the moſt approved Medical Authors, chiefly preſented by Mr. James, of the iſland of Jamaica ; to which Dr. Mead and other Gentlemen made very conſiderable additions : Alſo Anatomical cuts and two compleat Skeletons of different ſexes. This collection would have been very ſerviceable to a Profeſſor of Phyſic and Anatomy, when the revenues of the College ſhould have been ſufficient to ſubſiſt a gentleman in this character.—A few ancient and valuable Manuſcripts in different languages.—A pair of excellent new Globes of the largeſt ſize, preſented by Andrew Oliver, jun. Eſq;—A variety of Curioſities natural and artificial, both of American and foreign produce.—A font of Greek types (which, as we had not yet a printing-office, was repoſited in the library) preſented by our great benefactor the late worthy Thomas Hollis, Eſq; of London ; whoſe picture, as large as the life, and inſtitutions for two Profeſſorſhips and ten Scholarſhips, periſhed in the flames.——Some of the moſt conſiderable additions that had been made of late years to the library, came from other branches of this generous Family.

The library contained above five thouſand volumes, all which were conſumed, except a few books in the hands of the members of the houſe ; and two donations, one made by our late honorable Lieutenant Governor Dummer, to the value of 50 l. ſterling ; the other of 56 volumes, by the preſent worthy Thomas Hollis, Eſq; F. R. S. of London, to whom we have been annually obliged for valuable additions to our late library : Which donations, being but lately received, had not the proper boxes prepared for them ; and ſo eſcaped the general ruin.

As the library records are burnt, no doubt ſome valuable benefactions have been omitted in this account, which was drawn up only by memory.

Of the APPARATUS.

WHEN the late worthy THOMAS HOLLIS, Eſq; of London founded a Profeſſorſhip of Mathematics and Philoſophy in Harvard-College, he ſent a fine Apparatus for Experimental Philoſophy in its ſeveral Branches.

Under the head of *Mechanics*, there were machines for experiments of falling bodies, of the centre of gravity, and of centrifugal forces :—the ſeveral mechanical powers, balances of different ſorts, levers, pullies, axes in peritrochio, wedges, compound engines ; with curious models of each in braſs.

In *Hydroſtatics*, very nice balances, jars and bottles of various ſizes fitted with braſs caps, veſſels for proving the grand hydroſtatic Paradox, ſiphons, glaſs models of pumps, hydroſtatic balance, &c.

In *Pneumatics*, there was a number of different tubes for the Torricellian experiment, a large double-barrell'd Air-pump, with a great variety of receivers of different ſizes and ſhapes ; ſyringes, exhauſting and condenſing ; Barometer, Thermometer ; —with many other articles.

In *Optics*, there were ſeveral ſorts of mirrors, concave, convex, cylindric ; Lenſes of different foci ; inſtruments for proving the fundamental law of refraction ; Priſms, with the whole apparatus for the Newtonian theory of light and colors ; the camera obſcura, &c

And a variety of inſtruments for miſcellaneous purpoſes.

THE following articles were afterwards ſent us by Mr. Thomas Hollis, Nephew to that generous Gentleman, viz. an Orrery, an armillary Sphere, and a box of Microſcopes ; all of exquiſite workmanſhip.

For *Aſtronomy*, we had before been ſupplied with Teleſcopes of different lengths ; one of 24 feet ; and a braſs Quadrant of 2 feet radius, carrying a Teleſcope of a greater length ; which formerly belonged to the celebrated Dr. Halley. We had alſo the moſt uſeful inſtruments for Dialling ; and for *Surveying*, a braſs ſemicircle, with plain ſights and magnetic needle. Alſo, a curious teleſcope, with a complete apparatus for taking the difference of Level ; lately preſented by Chriſtopher Kilby, Eſq;

Many very valuable additions have of late years been made to this apparatus by ſeveral generous benefactors, whom it would be ingratitude not to commemorate here, as no veſtiges of their donations remain. We are under obligation to mention particularly, the late Sir Peter Warren, Knt. Sir Henry Frankland, Bart. Hon. Jonathan Belcher, Eſq; Lt. Governor of Nova-Scotia ; Thomas Hancock, Eſq; James Bowdoin, Eſq; Ezekiel Goldthwait, Eſq; John Hancock, A. M. of Boſton, and Mr. Gilbert Harriſon of London, Merchant. From theſe Gentlemen we received fine reflecting Teleſcopes of different magnifying powers ; and adapted to different obſervations ; Microſcopes of the ſeveral ſorts now in uſe ; Hadley's Quadrant fitted in a new manner ; a nice Variation Compaſs, and Dipping needle : with inſtruments for the ſeveral magnetical and electrical experiments—all new, and of excellent workmanſhip.——ALL DESTROYED !

Cambridge, Jan. 26. 1764. As the General Aſſembly have this day chearfully and unanimouſly voted to rebuild *Harvard*-Hall, it encourages us to hope, that the LIBRARY and APPARATUS will alſo be repaired by the private munificence of thoſe who wiſh well to America, have a regard for New-England, and know the importance of literature to the Church and State.

BOSTON: PRINTED BY R. AND S. DRAPER.

1764.

This broadside announcement of the fire was no doubt widely distributed.

The Library Is Rebuilt

Among the donors summoned forth by the fire John Hancock made the largest individual gift; with it 1,300 volumes were purchased. The province of New Hampshire gave funds that made possible the acquisition of 700 volumes, and many colonists, especially Bostonians, gave books or money.

The Library could not have been rebuilt so quickly, however, without numerous benefactors from England and Scotland, for whom Harvard College became the favorite colonial charity. As one of them, Nathaniel Lardner, wrote to Ezra Stiles in turning down a request for books for the Ecclesiastical Library in Newport, "For now the Harvard College is the object of the regard and attention of those who concern themselves for N.E., and in behalf of which we have received importunate requests from several, asking for a supply of books of all sorts and for mathematical instruments, etc."

The greatest donor by far during the eighteenth century was Thomas Hollis, the third Thomas Hollis to support the College and its Library. He had already sent numerous books, many of which survived the fire because they had not yet been unpacked. Hollis had his gifts handsomely bound and ornamented with a variety of emblematic tools, cut especially for him and intended to represent his "republican" tendencies.

The fund that he bequeathed in 1774 is the Library's oldest endowed book fund. It still buys books for Harvard.

This page from a list of books charged out at the time of the fire shows that many of the most prominent men in the Colony borrowed books — and were not faithful in returning them promptly.

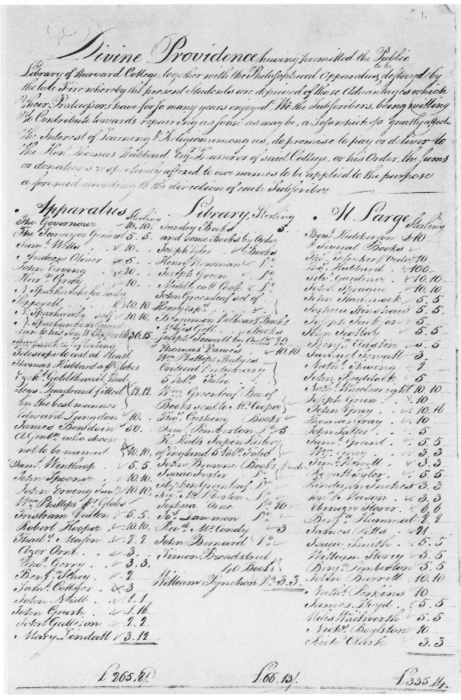

The first page of a list of donors of funds to replace the Library and the "philosophical apparatus," i.e. the scientific instruments.

16

Cameos of Thomas Hollis III and Thomas Brand Hollis,
with a book showing several of the ornaments with which
Thomas Hollis decorated bindings of books that he presented to Harvard.

1765

The Library Is Housed in a
New Harvard Hall

At the time of the fire the General Court was meeting and staying in Harvard Hall because of a smallpox epidemic in Boston. The legislature assumed responsibility for the loss and agreed to provide a replacement. It was finished in 1765. The Library, again placed on the second floor, had a greater proportion of the space. Along with rooms in which Hebrew and mathematics were taught, the floor housed the scientific instruments and miscellaneous natural history objects, which were "a great weariness to the showman, the librarian." The Library took over the entire floor in 1815, and it then had available a space 107-by-40-feet.

The Library as it probably looked in 1790.

View of the Colleges at Cambridge. Massachusetts.

Above: A view of Harvard Hall in 1792 before the additions to the front of the building; *below*: A plan of the second floor of Harvard Hall.

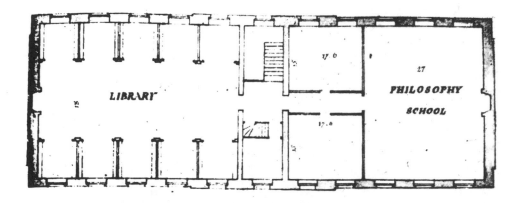

Librarians Try to Catalog
a Growing Collection

When collections of books arrived after the fire, the College authorities, grateful for the generosity of the donors, decided to keep together the books of each major gift. Thus, there was soon a Hancock alcove, a Hampshire alcove, and a Hollis alcove, plus alcoves for miscellaneous donations. This arrangement, in addition to acknowledging the donors, permitted shelves to be filled, whereas an alphabetical or subject arrangement, unless very loose, would have required that some space be left empty for inserting new acquisitions. This arrangement also served to get the books on the shelves with minimal labor.

In addition to a list of books saved from the old library, catalogs of the donations were soon prepared. Elegantly written, these catalogs might originally have been considered sufficient. No one knew, after all, that books would pour in from donors. But the flow of books continued, and soon, even if not immediately, a general alphabetical catalog was begun. Beginning with a book of blank paper, Librarian Andrew Eliot, Jr., wrote the letters of the alphabet at the head of pages and then copied in the entries from the donor catalogs. He was careful to leave some space for additions to be inserted. As new books arrived, they, too, were entered in the General Catalogue, which was sometimes called the Great Catalogue.

In 1768 the pages became too crowded, and a supplement was begun. It, too, by 1770, was filled. At this point the story temporarily becomes difficult to unravel. Two catalogs exist from the period. For one of them, known as the Mayhew catalog, the Corporation paid William Mayhew, librarian from 1769 to 1772, £5 for twenty-five days of "extraordinary services." The other, known as the Adams catalog, was the work of Amos Adams, minister of the First Church in Roxbury, who, as an Overseer and member of several committees on the Library, took his responsibilities so seriously that he wrote out catalogs.

	Size	Vol?	Edit:ⁿ	Setts
NB Jennings (David DD) Jewish Antiquities (a)	8	2	Lond	1766
Jennings (John)'s Discourses on preaching Christ (a)	12mo		Lond	1736
David Miscellanea in Usum Priv: Acad.				
Logica in Usum Juvent: Academ.				
(a) .... (John) Dis: on preaching Christ — ut: supra	12mo		Bost 1740	
(a) Jesuits, Moral Practices of	8vo		Lond 1690	
Jesuites La Morale des par un Dr de la Sorbonne	4to	35	Mons	1668
Act Historic Impartiale	12mo	2		1768
(a) Jesuitism (or their Discovery of the Mystery of)	8vo		Lond	1658
(a) Sewel's (Bn) Works	Folio		London	1811
Ditto Instruction (a Brief one in the Worship of God	8vo		Lond 1667	
(a) Introductio ad Lectionem Linguarum Orientalium	8vo		Lon 1655	
(a) Inventions, human, the Vanity of	8vo		Lond 1686	
Joannis (Glastoniensis) Chronica a Hearne	8vo	2	Ox 1726	
Jobi —ther in Versiculos Metrice Divisi, Cum Lat: Version	8vo			x
Johnson's Dictionary 2 Edt.	Folio	2	London	1755
Ditto 3 Edi:	Fol	2	Lond	1765
(Rev? Sam:) Works 2d Edition	Folio		London	1713
(Benj:) Works by Pet: Whalley	8vo	7	Lond	1756
....				
(a) Johnstoni Hist: Nat: de Piscibus				
(a) .... — Insectis				
(a) .... — Quadrupedibus	Fol	4	Francofurti	1650
(a) .... — Avibus				
Psalmi Davidici			Lon 1741	x
Jones (Row:) Postscript to the origin of Nations & Lang:	8vo		London	
(a) Jones's Vindication of S Matthew's Gosp:	8vo		Salop	1721
(a) — Canon	8vo	3	Lond	1726
Answer to the Essay on Spirit	8vo		London	1755
Essay on the first principles of nat: Philosophy	4to		Oxford	1762
Jones's Letter to a young Gentleman at Oxford —	8vo		London	1770
Jortin (John) Life of Erasmus	4to	2	Lond	1758
(a) Jortin's Life of Erasmus	11th	2	Lond	1758

The alphabetical catalog, begun in 1765 by Librarian Andrew Eliot, Jr. Because the catalog did not contain shelfmarks, the Librarian had to look in special lists to determine the location of books desired.

Ke

Hol. Kennet's Roman Antiquities   1.1.5.36

.. Keil Tentamina   8vo

Hol. Kennet's Sermons on 1any &c with Answers vc 1.3.5.33 4to

Hol. Kennet's Historical Register 1.2.2.13

.. Keebles Statutes at Large ———————————— folio

.. Keith (Geo) Revelation not ceased ———————— 8vo

.. Kempis (Tho.a) de imitatione Christi   12mo

Hol. Kerchmannus & alii de Annulis 1.2.8.56   12—

.. Kennicott Dissertations   Oxford   — 1753

.. Kennedy & Scripture Chronology   8vo

.. Kennicott on the Hebrew Text ————— 2 Vol. 8vo

Hau. Keil's Examination of Burnets & Whiston's Theory 8vo

Hau. —— Introduction to natural Philosophy   8vo

Hau. —— Astronomy   8vo

Hau. Kennet's (Bp.) Life   8vo

Hau. Keate Account of Geneva   12.

Hol. Kennet's Babel Lives of the Greek Poets 1.4.5.39 & Hau 8vo

Hau. Kempfer's History of Japan in English 2 Vol —— folio

Hau. ————— Exotics

.. Keys Travels Cuts ————————— 4 Vol —— 4to

.. Kennet's History of the Convocation

Haup. Keyslers Travels Cuts 1.3.24 ———— 4 Vol 4to

Haup. Kennet's History of England 3 Vols — 2.1.16. & Hol

Hol —— Kala (J.G.) Grammatica Hebræo. Harmonica   8vo

        Keckermanni opera. 2 copies   4to

        Kennet's Sermons   8vo
Hol —— Bibliotheca Americana primordia   4to

A page from the catalog of pamphlets, 1781.
It made accessible for the first time the pamphlets bound in volumes.

23

N.º D

+ . Middleton DD (Conyers) & Works,

+ ――――――――― Life of Cicero, 6 Edi:

a × ――――――――― Epistles of Cicero & Brutus,

a × ――――――――― Ditto ―

a ――――― Remarks on 2 Pamphlets ag.ᵗ him,

× ――――――――― 2 . Miscellanious Works,

+ ――――――――― 3 . Life of Cicero ―――

× מי הגיד מראש ונדעה .

+ . Middleton (Patrick) View of the Evidences of the Christ. Religion

× . Nihles & (Sam:) Medical Essays.

+ . Middleton (Patric.) Dissertation on the Power of the Church

a × . Mildmay Sir (Will.ᵐ/s Laws & Policy of England.ᵈ to Trade,

. Millar of Jn.º of his Observations concerning the Distinction of Banks,
                                                                in Society

+ . Miller (Philip)s Gardiner's Dictionary, with Cutts,
        ^

+ . Miller's   Account of the university of Cambridge
                              ^

+ . Miller (John)s Ten Curious prints of Insects & Plants,

+ . Miller (Tho.) Nobilitas Anglica

+ . Mills (John) on the Management of Bees,

+ . Millii (Dav.) Dissertationes Selecta ――――――

+ . Millii (Davidii) Dissertationes selectæ,

+ . Mill (Eugenii) Novum Testamentum Græcum ――― 2 Edi
+ . Milner (John) Sermons

+ . Milton (John) & Paradise lost, 2 Edi

+ ――――― Paradise lost. Lat. & Eng:

――――― Ditto ―

+ ――――― Ditto ― 4 Edi:

―――――― Paradisus amissa, with the Eng: original,

+ ――――― Il Paradiso perduto, tradotto, di P. Rolli

+ ――――― Le Paradis perdue & reconquis de-traduit
                                          p. Langlois

The Adams catalog, initially the work of an Overseer.

Mag	Tom	Locus	Tempus	Class	Mr	Lib	Donor
4to	4	Lond:	1752	2	1	4	14	Hollis
4to	2	Lond:	1757	2	2	4	17	Hollis
8vo		Lond:	1743	1	4	6	32	Hancock
8vo		Lond:	1743	4	4	6	5	Hollis
8vo		Lond	748					
4to	4	Lond	1752	5	2	4	16	
4to	2	Lond	1741	5	2	4	20	
8vo		Amst:		8				
8vo		London	—	7	4	6	22	
8vo	2	Lond:	1745	7	1	6	20	Wm James
8vo		Lond:	1733	7	4	6	32	
4to		Lond:	1766	3	3	5	12	N. Hunt:
4to		Lond:	1771	4	1	4		J. Smith Es
Fol		Lond:	1719	3	2	1	13	N. Hunt
8vo		Lond:	1717	4	1	8	12	Hollis
Fol		Lond:	1764	2	3	1	4	Hollis
Fol		Lond:	1608	4	3	4	11	do
8vo		Lond:	1766	2	4	6	4	Hollis
11mo		Atheni	1724	9	2	8	11	
4to		Lug: Bat:	1743	4	1	7	32	Hollis
8vo		Lond	1746	5	4	7	21	Hollis
12mo		Lond:	1674	4	2	3	16	Hollis
4to		Lond:	1686	2	4	7	8	Hollis
4to		Lond:	1686	2	4	7	9	Hollis
Fol		Lond:	1688	2	4	2	2	Hollis
4to		Lond:	1676	2	4	7	8	Hollis
Fol	e.	Parigi	1742	2	4	1	13	Hollis
12mo	9	Paris	1743	2	1	7	41	Hollis

It had shelfmarks, which enabled the Librarian to determine easily
the location of books, and it recorded the source of the books.

Both the General Catalogue and the Mayhew catalog lacked full shelfmarks; the Adams catalog has them and records donors as well. Although these catalogs have in the past been seen as successive catalogs, they may well have been in use concurrently, one serving as a public catalog and the other as the librarian's catalog.

The latest entry in the Adams catalog is for Mather Byles's sermons received in September 1774. After that the Library seems to have developed another cataloging backlog, for on 3 April 1775, the Corporation voted "that the Librarian be allowed for himself and assistants in Cataloging the Books in the Library to the amount of seventy-four days work, viz., 2027 Books numbered in the vacation last Winter, besides others, the sum of twelve pounds." The reference to numbering suggest that the books were recorded in the alcove shelf-lists. It seems likely that another alphabetical catalog would have been written out, but the Library was dismantled, with some of the books set up in Concord. The next catalog, for which the College Butler, Phillips Payson, a graduate of the class of 1778, was paid £120, was completed by 2 June 1779. Only a fragment of one leaf remains. Beautifully written, it included shelfmarks.

Payson's work was considered satisfactory, for he was then engaged to record the contents of volumes of pamphlets, or tracts as they were then called. None had been listed in earlier catalogs. From Payson's working copy, a transcribed version was completed in May 1781. The Library then had a catalog of all its holdings, save accessions since 1779. But such a happy state could not last long in a growing library. By 1787 a new catalog was needed, and the exasperation of the College authorities is suggested by the Corporation vote of 1 November 1787, "that the Committee for inspecting the Library be desired to take such measures for compleating the catalogue as they shall think best." What they thought best is not known, but in 1789 work began on a new catalog.

Cataloging the Library in the second half of the eighteenth century required a considerable financial expenditure that threatened to escalate as the Library grew. The £12 paid for cataloging in 1775 is close to 1 percent of £1550, the estimated total income of the College in 1774. Moreover, that work seems to have been only preliminary to a full catalog.

It might appear that the arrangement by donor (rather than by author or by subject) created the basic difficulty, for with a donor arrangement it was necessary to maintain the alcove catalogs, which recorded the books as they stood on the shelves, even though that work did nothing to further access by readers. Moreover, the shelflist for alcove 10, where new acquisitions were placed, had to be redone three times in the eighteenth century. The other side of the donor arrangement, however, is that only the shelflist for alcove 10 had to be redone. Had the basic arrangement been otherwise, all would have had to be redone. The donor arrangement was not an irrational or even unfortunate solution. Since the Library had earlier been classified by subject, the donor arrangement may even have entailed conscious rejection of subject classification, based on knowledge of its problems.

Joseph Green Cogswell (Librarian from 1821 to 1823) found one part of the solution to the repetitive work — a catalog written out on individual leaves which could be held together in sheaves. In a sheaf catalog, only individual leaves need to be recopied. Even at that date, Cogswell's successor found his solution radical and copied the sheets into a manuscript book catalog.

Even if the traditional form of the catalog had been changed in the eighteenth century, that would not have relieved the College of repeatedly paying the costs for cataloging. Except during the first half dozen years after the fire a catalog was considered the product of concentrated activity during a specific period, not the result of cumulative effort over time.

In 1787 the College demonstrated awareness that cumulative effort was required, for on 24 July the Corporation voted "that every Librarian in future, insert in the general Catalogue such books as come into the Library from time to time, as well as enter them in the Alcove Catalogues where they may be placed, which shall be considered as one part of the duty of his Office."

The Corporation's vote did not guarantee that the task would be carried out. At least as late as 1830 the Corporation found it necessary to instruct the librarian to open packages of books within ten days of receipt, check the books against the list supplied by the bookseller, and enter the books in the catalogs. The librarian so instructed was the eleventh since 1787. Even though he (Benjamin Peirce) was devoted to the Library, the increasing demands of the post, along with the rapid turnover, continued to make cataloging a thorny problem.

1765

Certain Books Prohibited

The Library seems to have put on its shelves, with thanks, all titles not already in the Library, and most duplicates as well, but it did restrict some. The list, begun in 1765 and in use up to 1789, that records gifts of Thomas Hollis in the order in which they stood on the shelves noted that P meant "absolute prohibition" and that an * designated a book prohibited "to undergraduates." It is difficult to read some entries, but there seem to be three absolute prohibitions and of them only one book that would have been considered dangerous, Francis Hutcheson's *Moral Philosophy* (1759). Many more were prohibited to undergraduates. Along with books that were considered injurious to the faith or morals of undergraduates, dictionaries and other reference works did not circulate, presumably for the same reason that they cannot today be removed from Widener; some books, particularly books with plates, did not circulate because of their value, and others had limited circulation because of the fear that students would use them as ponies.

Prohibited books

All Dictionaries, books of plates & maps
[reference being had to law 16th of Ch: 8 J.

Bolingbroke's Works
Shaftesbury
Hume's Essays
Rowe's Works vol. I.
Mandeville's Fable of the Bees.
Addison's Works 2nd vol. 4to.
All Manuscripts
Birch's Lives & Heads
Hume's Engl. in 6.2.6.1&9, unless
the wished for vol. gone from 8.2.5 & 1.2.3.
Albertus de Sec. mul.
Astruc on Vener. Diseases
——— on Diseases of Women
Armstrong on Do.
Friend's Emmenologia & the Trans. by D &c.
La Motte's Midwifery
White on Pregnancy
Whyte on Histeric Disorders.

This list, though undated, was probably drawn up between 1785 and 1790.

1773

Harvard Publishes the First Library
Catalog for Undergraduates

In 1773 Harvard published the first list of books recommended for undergraduates. Twenty-seven pages in length and alphabetically arranged, it had a preface in Latin, which translates:

Inasmuch as the Catalogue of Books in the College Library, embracing Books in almost all Tongues and about all Sciences and Arts, most of which are above the Comprehension of Younger Students, is very long and not to be completely unrolled, when Occasion demands, save at very great expense of time, it has seemed wise to put together a briefer Catalogue, to wit, of Books which are better adapted to their use. In the following Catalogue, then, in addition to Classical Authors, there are included Books chiefly in the vernacular and belonging to the general culture of the mind, omitting as much as possible those which are in daily use in the College, as also those which are written in foreign Languages, or which treat of specialized Disciplines, e.g., Medicine or Jurisprudence. But let no one infer from this that Students are debarred from the freer use of the Library.

Although this preface implies that the books had been specially selected, they were actually for the most part duplicates that had come in with the great outpouring of gifts after the fire of 1764.

Not all undergraduates could borrow these books, only seniors and juniors, both of which classes could also borrow from the "great Library" with appropriate permission. In the fall of 1795 sophomores were given the right to borrow books; freshmen followed in 1814.

Hopkins's (Bp) Works, Fol	9	4 2	9	
on the Covenant, 8vo	9	3 7	24	
Horatii Opera,—cum Notis Bentleii, 4to	7	1 4	22	
Horseley's (John) Roman Antiquities of Britain, Fol	2	4 2	9	
Houghton (John) Introduction, to EnglishGrammar, 12mo	2	4 8	3	
Howe's (John) Works, Fol 2 vols	5			
Howell's (William) History of the World, Fol	8			
Hughes's (Griffith) Natural History of Barbados, Fol	10			
Hume's (David) History of England, 4to 6 vols	1	2 3	5	
Hungary--Account of the Kingdom of--8vo	7	1 8	49	
Hutcheson's L L D (Fra.) Moral Philosophy, 4to 2 vols	5	3 4	2	
His other Works.				
Hutchinson's (Governor) History of the Massachusetts-				
Bay, 8vo 2 vols	7	1 5	16	
D D (Francis) on Witchcraft, 8vo	7	4 6	21	

I

Jackson's (Richard) Literatura Græca, 12mo	6	1		
Japan—History of—by Kæmpfer, Fol 2 vols	1	4 1	4	
Idler, 12mo, 2 vols. by Johnson.	1	1 9	2	
Jenkins, D D (Robert) Reasonableness of Christianity,				
8vo 2 vols	7	3 7	16	
Jennings D D (David)--All his Works.				
(John) on Preaching Christ 12mo	9	2 8	42	
Indostan,--History of--4to	1	1 3	6	
Inquisition (Portuguese)--Memoirs of the--8vo	1	3 6	7	
Jones's (Jeremiah) Method of Settling the Canon of the				
New-Testament, 8vo 3 vols	7	1 6	24	
Jortin, D D (John) all his Works.				
Josephus, Fol	7	3 2	6	
Italy—A Journey to—12mo	2	2 7	34	
Julian (The Emperor)—Life of—8vo	5			
Justiniani Institutiones, 4to.	4	2 4	1	
Justini Martyris Opera, Fol	7	2 1	20	
Juvenalis et Persius, 4to	7	1 4	13	

K.

Kaim's (Ld) on Criticism, 8vo 3 vols	8	3		
Keate's Account of Geneva, 12mo	1	3 8	10	
Keill's, M D (John) Examination of Burnet's and Whis-				
ton's Theories, 8vo.	1	3 4	29	
Introduction to Natural Philosophy, 8vo	1	3 4	6	
Astronomy, 8vo	1	3 4	21	
	Kennet's			

A page from the first catalog of books for undergraduates, 1773.
The catalog contains 800 entries.

1775

A Harvard Library Book Helps
Defeat the British

On 3 February 1775, "by order of the Provincial Congress," the Harvard Library loaned David Cheever, a member from Charlestown of the Provincial Congress, John Muller's *Treatise on Artillery*, 2d ed. (London, 1768). Exactly one week before the British marched to Lexington and Concord on 19 April 1775, Abraham Watson of Cambridge, also a member of the Provincial Congress, borrowed the same book. He kept it throughout the early years of the Revolution. Perhaps the book saw such heavy service that it was badly damaged; it was no longer in the Library in 1790.

This specific case of notable use is not cited to imply that the Harvard Library has served as a public library. It has not, in the sense of today's public libraries, but the Library has always made — and continues to make — its resources available to others. In 1830 Librarian Benjamin Peirce described the policy on access:

> Books are loaned to all the Undergraduates, to the Members of the Theological and Law Schools, to all persons residing in Cambridge for purposes of study, to the Members of the Faculty, Corporation, and Board of Overseers, and to all regularly ordained Clergymen living within ten miles of the College; and persons, not coming within the provisions of the law, may, by application to the Corporation, obtain the use of any books, which are proper to be taken from the Library. The privileges, granted to individuals, are not exceeded by those enjoyed at any other institution of a similar kind, and are believed to be in all respects as great as a due regard to general accommodations and to the preservation of the books would permit.

It is not possible to state succinctly the current policies of the various Harvard libraries, but the last sentence of Peirce's statement is arguably still true. Hundreds of thousands of rare books and millions of manuscripts are in non-circulating collections. Scholars who need to see those materials may freely do so.

The loans made "by order of the Provincial Congress" are recorded
at the top of the last page of this charging book for the years 1773 to 1782.
Books such as this exist, with a few gaps, from 1762 to 1897.

1775

The Harvard Library
Moves to Concord

In 1775, when the British troops occupied Boston, the patriots set up headquarters in Cambridge. (General George Washington for a short time had his headquarters in Wadsworth House, where the Office of the Director of the University Library is now located.) The Provincial Congress commandeered the Harvard buildings and ordered the Library and philosophical apparatus to be moved to Andover for safety. Even occupation by friendly troops threatened the Library, for the danger of accidental fire was heightened. There was also the possibility that the British troops would burn Harvard buildings.

After debating where the College should reassemble, the Corporation and Overseers decided on Concord, where some boxes of books were unpacked and arranged in the house of Humphrey Barrett. The catalog of the library in Concord and the record of its use are preserved in the University Archives.

On 21 June 1776 the College reassembled at her "ancient seat," though not all books were returned from their various locations until late in 1778. The Harvard Library was fortunate, unlike the Library of Congress, which was burned by the British in 1814.

Humphrey Barrett's home in Concord, which held the Harvard Library
at the beginning of the Revolutionary War. The house no longer exists.

Harvard Publishes a
Classified Catalog

The Library laws adopted in 1765 contained a regulation that had been ignored:

A written catalogue of all the Books in each Alcove, shall be hung up therein; And an alphabetic Catalogue of the whole Library, divided into Chapters, according to the Diversity of Subjects, shall be printed and a Copy chain'd in each Window of the Library. There shall also be an Account of the Donors, open to every Ones inspection, to begin with the Donors to the former Library.

Perhaps stimulated by the existence of that regulation, in early 1789 Librarian Isaac Smith, assisted by Thaddeus Mason Harris (Librarian from 1791 to 1793), Hezekiah Packard, and Stephen Sewell (Hancock Professor of Hebrew and Other Oriental Languages from 1764 to 1785), was engaged in compiling a new type of catalog. In the resulting Catalogue of books belonging to the Library of the University, the books were listed under sixty different "heads."

A classified catalog that one might wish to pore over needed, more than an alphabetical one, to be available in multiple copies, and on 6 April 1790 work began on preparing it for printing. Of the printed work, twenty-four copies were kept for use in the Library. Copies were also placed in the entries to the dormitories.

The 1790 catalog lacked a general alphabetical listing by author. Moreover, the Library still faced the problem of keeping the catalog up-to-date. It did this by interleaving copies and annotating them. At least as late as 1822 an annotated copy was used for the Visiting Committee's inventory.

CATALOGUS

BIBLIOTHECÆ HARVARDIANÆ

CANTABRIGIÆ

NOV - ANGLORUM.

BOSTONIÆ:

Typis Thomæ et Johannis Fleet,

MDCCXC.

Title page of the 1790 catalog, which contained 9800 entries.
On pp. 38-39 are reproduced facing pages of an interleaved copy,
which record changes to the holdings.

37

Bonefonius (Joannes) Carmina 10mo Lond. 1720.

4.4.9. Boothby (Ser Brooke) Fables & Satires 12mo.

4.4.9. Brown (Wm L. DD.) Philemon, or the progress of virtue a
Svo 2 vols. Edinb. 1809.

7.1.7. Brown (Thos.) Renovation of India a Poem with the Prophecy
of Ganges an ode. 12mo Edinb. 1808.

7.5.26. Cowper (Wm) Poems 12 mo 2 vols Phil. 1803

9.1.3. Crabbe (George) The Borough 2 copies

14.3.7.6. Cumberland (R) Retrospection 12mo Boston 1812.

5.1.26. Cumberland (R.) Exodiad. 4to Lond. 1807.

2.4.9. Delille (J.) Oeuvres 12mo 13 tom. Paris. 1804.

3.4.7. Drummond (Wm Hamilton.) Lucretius 1st book trd. 8vo
Edinb. 1808. —

4.2.3.9. Darwin's Temple of Nature 8vo
7.1.4.

3.5.2. Elton (Charles A.) translation of Hesiod into English verse.
3.4.8. 12mo Lond. 1809 —

5.2.21. Epithalamia Oxoniensia sive Gratulationes in augustissimi
10.4.1.20b. regis Georgii III. illustrissimo principesse Sophiæ Charlottæ
7.2.2. nuptias auspicatissimas. fol. 2 vol. Oxon 1761.

10.73.7.25. Family Tablet. 12 mo

14.3.5.4. Fessenden (T. G.) Terrible Tractoration 8vo

14.3.7.5. —— (—) Original Poems 12 mo

14.3.7.4. —— (—) Democracy Unveiled. 12 mo

3.5.26. Gesner (S.) New Idylls, or Pastoral Poems. 12mo Phil. 1802

14.3.7.30. Graham's Birds of Scotland 12 mo
7.1.

Boscovich (Reg.) De solis et lunæ defectibus poema, 4to, Lond. 1760. 2.2.4.6.&11.
(2 copies)
Brooke (Ld) Certain elegant and learned works, 4to, Lon.1633.(2cop.) 2.4.4.13 & 6.1.3.2c   3.1.6
Browne (I. Hawkins) Poems, lat. et eng. 4to, Lond. 1768. 4.3.5.2c
Buchanan (Geo.) Paraphrasis psalmorum, 12mo, Raphel. 1609.
Butler (S.) Hudibras, by Grey, 8vo, 2d ed. 2 vol. Lond. 1764. 1.1.7.19 sold
Caro (Annibal.) Rime, 8vo, Venet. 1572. 4.4.5.111.
Champion (Joseph) Poems of Ferdosi, trd 4to, Calcutta, 1785. 12.2.10.
[v. Orient. Lit.]
Chapman (Geo.) The Iliads of Homer, trd into eng. verse, fol.Lon.1610 9.3.3/
Chaucer (Geof.) Works, by J. Urry, fol. Lond. 1721. 1.3.1.1.
Churchill (Cha.) Poems, 4to, 2d ed. Lond. 1765. 2 vols. 1.1.3.27
Cooke (Tho.) Poetical transl. of the works of Hesiod, 4to, Lond.1728. 4.4.5.5
— — — 12mo, 2d ed. — 1740. 9.4.0.11
[v. Auct. Class. Hesiod.]
Cooper (J. Gilb.) Poems on several subjects, 12mo, Lond. 1764. 6.1.0.19   2.4.7.44
Cowley (Abr.) Works, 8vo, 3 vol. 10th ed. Lond. 1707. 1.4.7.0
Craddock (Tho.) Version of the psalms, 8vo, Anapolis, 1756. 0.1.0.5
Croce (G. Cæf.) Descrizione della vita, et opere, 4to, Veron. 1738. 2.3.5.20
Denham (Jn.) Poems, and translations, with the Sophy, 8vo, 4th ed. 1.4.7.17
Lond. 1703.
Dodd (Wm.) Hymns of Callimachus, trd into english verse, &c. 9.2.3.1.
4to, Lond. 1755. [v. Auct. Class. Calim.]
Doddridge (Phil.) Hymns, 12mo, Lond. 1766. 3d edit. 6.2.0.29
——— Principles of the christian religion in plain easy verse 6.2.0.31
for the use of children, 12mo, Lond. 1767.
Dodsley (Rob.) Collection of poems, 12mo, 6 vol. Lond. 1763. 1.3.0.42
Dryden (Jn.) Miscellany, 8vo, 6 vol. Lond. 1702. 2.1.6.40
——— Virgil in eng. verse, 8vo, 3d ed. 3 vol. Lond. 1709. 1.3.7.2
Duck (Steph.) Poems on several occasions, 8vo, 4th ed. — 1764. 1.1.0.11   7.2.0.32
Epigrammata et poematia vetera, 12mo, Paris, 1590. 2.4.0.23
Falconer (Wm.) Shipwreck, 8vo, Lond. 1769. 3.3.0.2
Fletcher (Phineas) The purple island, or the isle of Man; together 13.1.7.20 published
with piscatorie ecloges, &c. 4to, Camb. 1633.
Francis (Php.) Poetical translation of Horace,12mo,4 vol.Lond.1750. 7.1.0.39
[v. Auct. class. Horat.]
Free (John) Poems and miscellaneous pieces, 8vo,   Lond. 1751. 6.1.7.13   2.2.5.9
——— 2d ed. — 1757. 6.11.0.41   2.4.7.46
Gaetanus (Æneas) La peste di Messina accaduta nell' anno 1743, 0.1.0.
in versi, 12mo, Venet. 1747.
Garth (Sir Sam.) Dispensatory, 12mo, 9th edit. Lond. 1726. 4.2.0.8
——— 10th ed. — 1741. 1.4.0.2
——— Ovid's Metamorphoses, trd by Dryden and others; 7.2.0.21
published by Garth, 12mo, 5th ed. 2 vol. Lond.1751. 1.2.3.41.
Gay (John) Poems on several occasions, 4to, Lond. 1720. 4.1.5.6.
Glover (Rich.) Leonidas, 4to, Lond. 1736. 4.2.0.16.
——— 12mo, — 1738.

The Overseers Visiting Committee Takes the Annual Inventory

The Board of Overseers Committee to Visit the Library is the mechanism by which the Board oversees the Library. The institution goes back at least to 1766. The earliest existing separate report of a Board of Overseers Visiting Committee is from 1799.

The reports show that the long-standing, overriding concern about the Library was security: that the books be on the shelves and in "neat order." In 1799 the Committee met in the Library during the summer recess and actually took an inventory to verify that the librarian had maintained the collection intact and in good condition. Each year it did the same — until 1854 when, faced with the magnitude of the task, it gave up and agreed to rely on spot checks and inventories taken by librarians. Thanks to the acquisition of several large collections, the books purchased with the Subscribed Fund of 1842, and John Langdon Sibley's aggressive begging over more than a decade, the Library had grown too large for an inventory to be taken by outsiders.

In the same decade the Committee expanded its role and reported on other issues facing the Library.

Cambridge July 9. 1799.

The Com.ᵉᵉ appointed to visit and instruct the Library &c. beg leave to report that they have attended that Service, and that they found the books in the _Library_ in their places and in very neat order, that none were missing but what were ~~~~ accounted for, — and that 43 Columes have been presented to the Library, & 11 purchased for it.

It gives them pain to add that the following Gentlemen are delinquent in returning their books—

     Dr Eckley

     Mr. Kirkland &

     Mr. Pipon.

The articles in the _Museum_ were found handsomely disposed & in good preservation. The only article added to it since the last Visitation is the Skin of a large wolf, stuffed, — presented by Benjᵐ Vaughan Esq.

In the _Philosophical Apparatus_ all the instrumᵗˢ &c. were found, neatly kept, & whole.

To the Cabinet of Minerals have been added a few Specimens of American Ores. —

The Chymical _room_ was found in its usual state, excepting that it appeared to have been broken open, & several articles stolen, viz

  Wedgewood's thermometer, with its case & pieces of clay.

A report of a Committee of the Overseers in 1799.
It records that the Librarian had kept the books in "neat order."

A Librarian Establishes the Second Endowed Book Fund

The Library received its second endowed book fund in 1801, a bequest from Samuel Shapleigh, class of 1789 and librarian from 1793 to 1800. Shapleigh clearly perceived that the Library's major need was for regular purchases of new books, since he specified that the income was to be spent "for the purchase of such modern publications as shall improve the Students in polite literature . . . and to consist of Poetry and Prose but neither in Greek nor Latin."

Numerous other librarians have been major benefactors of the institution in which they worked. In addition to current-use gifts of money and gifts in kind, many have established endowed funds to support acquisitions or the work of the Library. Librarians have also been honored by funds established in their names.

Bought with
THE INCOME FROM
THE BEQUEST OF
SAMUEL SHAPLEIGH,
(Class of 1789,)
LATE LIBRARIAN OF
HARVARD COLLEGE,
July 29, 1861.

A bookplate of the Library's second endowed fund.
Established by bequest of Librarian Samuel Shapleigh,
the fund continues to buy books for the Library today.

Library Acquisitions
Reach a Low Point

Additions to the Library in 1806-07 were particularly few in number. Had a large book sale taken place, the Library would probably have acquired more. A committee would have been formed, lists of books looked over, decisions made, and the books purchased. Except when such opportunities arose, few purchases were made. They were, for the most part, periodicals and multi-volume reference works, materials for which an immediate need existed. Decisions were made by the Corporation.

Change took place on 21 February 1814, when the Corporation delegated power by voting "that a Committee for the purchase of Books be annually chosen, at the meeting next after the settlement of the Treasurer's accounts." It was further ordered "that it shall be the first care of the said Committee to supply the Library with an adequate number of Books suitable for under Graduates and the Resident Graduates, and also such Books as may be proper for the Instructers in particular departments." The Committee was to proceed by preparing a list of books in the order of their importance. The President and William Ellery Channing, also a member of the Corporation, were its first members. At least as late as 1842 members of the Corporation still made up the Committee. Definitely by 1856, it included members of the faculty.

The Committee seems to have furthered regular acquisitions, for in 1828 the librarian was instructed to prepare monthly lists of acquisitions. In 1821 there first began to be kept the "Librarian's Wastebook," which recorded acquisitions in brief form; a more formally kept series of volumes recording books received was begun in 1827.

Despite these steps toward comprehensive and systematic acquisitions, the funds available were small, and they continued to be spent primarily on occasions of unusual opportunity.

The following books have been added to the Library since the last examination.

Dufief's Nature Displayed in two volumes 8vo by the author.

Holme's Septuagint 1 vol. fol. by the Corporation.

A Greek copy of Daniel's prophecies fol. by the Corporation.

Dr. Blaney's Zechariah 4to by the Corporation.

Bishop Horsley's Hosea 4to by the Corporation

Two copies of the 5th vol. of Marshall's Life of Washington and two Maps belonging to the work through the hand of the Treasurer.

Ludwig's German Dictionary in two volumes 4to by the Corporation

The numbers of the Monthly Anthology to the present time by the Editors

Nicholson's Journal of natural philosophy, chemistry, and the arts in 10 vol. 8vo by the Corporation

Laws and regulations of the State Prisons by Mr. Jackson 10?

Dr. Rees new Cyclopaedia 14 number 4to by the author.

June 4. 1807

On this page are recorded all of the Library's acquisitions for 1806-07.

Freshmen Are Given Permission to Borrow Books — From a Selected List

In 1814 freshmen were first permitted to borrow books from the Library, but only those on a selected list; and they could take out a book in English only if they borrowed at the same time one in Greek or Latin. Each freshman could borrow books only on every third Friday afternoon. By no means did all avail themselves of the opportunity.

This seemingly progressive step may have been more a political maneuver than a commitment to making books available to all. The next year, Librarian Andrews Norton, at the request of President Kirkland, prepared a report urging the formation of two distinct libraries, one for undergraduates. The reasons put forth ranged from the need to preserve valuable books to faculty complaints about "the number of students in the Library, many of whom come in from mere curiosity." A "students' library" was, indeed, formed. It had about 3,000 volumes at the time the new Gore Hall library opened in 1841, but it was inhospitably housed in the area that served as the reading room and librarian's office, as well as the delivery room, coat room, and main entrance hall.

Although students were not limited to that collection, their access to the other books was restricted. Not until Lamont opened in 1949 were the needs of undergraduates fully met.

✓ Fitzosborne's Letters, 12mo.

Spectator, 8 vols. 12mo.

Guardian, 2 vols. 12mo.

Adventurer, 4 vols. 12mo.

Observer, 4 vols. 12mo.

Avantures du Télemaque, 2 tom. 12mo.

Travels of Anacharsis, 4 vols. 8vo.

✓ Goldsmith's History of the Earth and Animated Nature, 4 vols. 8vo.

Edgeworth's Popular Moral and } Tales, Fashionable and other works.

———

Price's Dissertations.

Watts on the Improvement of the mind.

———

Religious Works.

The Bible, in different languages.

Paley's Natural Theology, 8vo.

Fenelon, Demonstration de l'existence de dieu,12mo.

Derham's Astro-Theology, 8vo.

————— Physico-Theology, 8vo.

Paley's Evidences of Christianity, 8vo.

————— Horæ Paulinæ, 8vo.

Bogue's Essay on the authority of the New Testament, 12mo.

Priestley on the Evidences of Revealed Religion, 3 vols. 8vo.

Above: A page from the *Catalogue of Books, Which May Be Taken from the Library of Harvard University by Members of the Freshman Class* (Cambridge, 1814). Even the printed documents of Harvard's history are often exceedingly rare; no copy of this catalog was in the Archives until 1963.
Left: The charging record showing one freshman's reading.

1816

President Kirkland Appeals to Publishers for Gifts of Books

The earliest printed appeal for gifts, first sent out by President John T. Kirkland in 1816, reflected concern for acquiring current publications but sought to get them as gifts. Gifts would have made up for the lack in the United States of a comprehensive, current booktrade journal recording new publications. Gifts would also have relieved the Library of the burden of decisions and of the time-consuming work of placing orders.

The appeal for gifts of books rather than money reflected as well the tradition of the Library. Gifts of books were largely responsible for its growth, and they continued for decades to exceed purchases during most years.

The Visiting Committee report in 1866 contained a summary of acquisitions since the fire. The excess of purchased volumes over gifts between 1832 and 1850 reflects less a trend toward purchases than a bulge resulting from the expenditure of the Donation Fund of 1842.

Acquisitions

Year	Books and Volumes			Pamphlets		
	Purchases	Gifts	Total	Purchases	Gifts	Totals
1764–1790		462				
1791–1823		393				
1823–1831		625				
1832–1850	862	419	1,281	108	1,204	1,312
1851–1858	769	1,468	2,237	221	2,255	2,476
1859–1866	1,870	2,146	4,016	458	4,922	5,380
1832–1866	1,071	1,054	2,125	214	2,294	2,508

Madam, Harvard University, Cambridge, Mass. January, 18**.** 337

THE Corporation of this University are desirous of placing in the public Library of the University one or more copies of the books, and periodical works and pamphlets published in our country, especially of those which are valuable. But although they are annually considerable purchasers of literary works, it cannot be supposed within their ability to buy more than a small proportion of the whole number issued. They are therefore induced to request publishers to present to the Library copies of the works, which they may respectively cause to be printed. The great present value of our Library, its situation near the metropolis of New England, the liberal manner in which the use of it is extended, it being kept open six hours of each secular day, the care bestowed on its preservation and embellishment, its connexion with this ancient Seminary, and the consideration that by the exercise of liberality here suggested a great benefit must accrue to the cause of literature and science and to the particular interests of your profession with little comparative expense or burden to any individual, lead us to think that our application will not appear unsuitable or be unwelcome. Relying upon your enlightened zeal for the dignity and advancement of good learning, and your candid construction of this request, we beg leave to mention, that any books, or pamphlets, of recent or earlier date, which you may be willing to present, will reach their destination, if directed to the University, to the Librarian, or President at Cambridge, and committed to the care of

or sent to

Boston.

Your donations will be regularly acknowledged, and entered, with the name of the donor, in a Record Book, always kept open for inspection in the Library.

Your obedient servant,

John T. Kirkland Pres't.

This appeal for gifts, printed in 1816, was in use at least until 1827.
This copy was sent to Catherine Maria Sedgwick in Stockbridge.
It resulted in the gift of three of her novels.

1817

The Law School Promises
"a complete law library"

In 1817, when the Law School first offered instruction, it attempted to entice students away from the traditional practice of study in a private law office by promising "access to a complete law library." That library, formed by purchase and transfer from the College Library, fit into a professor's office. Nine years later, in 1826, it had 584 titles, still not "complete." By 1846, though it had only 11,000 volumes, the Visiting Committee reported that the Law Library was unsurpassed in the Union. It has remained so, and it may also be considered preeminent in the world.

The Law School Library's great period of growth began after the appointment of Christopher Columbus Langdell as dean in 1870. He pioneered the use of the case system in teaching law and believed that the library was to law students as the laboratory is to scientists. Langdell hired the first full-time librarian and supported him in building a comprehensive collection of the common law of the English-speaking world.

English collections continued to be acquired in the twentieth century, particularly the Dunn collection of early English law in 1913, an acquisition which made the Harvard Law Library unrivaled in this field. But the scope of the collection vastly expanded: in 1903, the Brinton Coxe collection of Roman and canon law; 1905, the Barnard collection of portraits and the Muzio Melloni library; 1911, the Francis Rawle collection of bar association proceedings; 1912, the 14,000-volume Olivart library of international law; 1913, virtually complete holdings of the legislation and court decisions of the Latin American countries, purchased by Dr. Walter Lichtenstein on a buying trip; 1920, the Sellier collection of criminology in the Continental languages; 1921, the Paul Viollet French legal history collection, the Lammasch collection of criminal and international law, a

Dane Hall, built in 1832, housed the Law Library for half a century. It stood on the site now occupied by Lehman Hall and faced on Harvard Square.

Above: Law School students in the Austin Hall reading room before 1909;
below: Law School students in the Langdell Hall reading room in the 1980s.

collection of Russian law to the end of the Kerensky regime, and the Arthur von Briesen collection of legal aid documents; 1925, a large collection of Brazilian legislation and decisions; 1927, the J. E. de Becker collection of Japanese law; 1931, collections of the laws of the states in the different federal republics in Latin America; 1932, the 8,000-volume legal portion of the Stolberg family library, plus 8,000 theses, the criminological library of Alexander Loeffler, and the Landsberg library of German law; 1937, 25,000 French edicts from the library of Loménie de Brienne.

Much more could be noted: Indian law fills rows and rows of stacks, and Chinese law is represented by many early books; the Art Collection has 3,000 prints and 20,000 photographs; the Manuscript Division has a large collection of papers of Oliver Wendell Holmes, Jr., and other giants in American law. But the point has been made. The Law School, now with more than 1.4 million books, kept the promise made in 1817.

1818

A Salem Merchant Gives Harvard
Its First Research Collection

The Harvard Library has been called a collection of collections, each of them adding research strength, perhaps even unique material. The first research collections added were in the field of American history.

In 1818 the Salem merchant Israel Thorndike bought for Harvard the collection of Americana formed by Daniel Christoph Ebeling, a professor of commerce in Hamburg. Before Thorndike, many individuals had given valuable books, but this was the first collector's library to be acquired by Harvard. Along with 10,000 maps, now the nucleus of the Map Collection, the Ebeling Library had 3,200 volumes. These included bound American newspapers, some issues of which exist only in the collection of the German professor.

Five years later, in 1823, Harvard's treasurer, Samuel A. Eliot, acquired for Harvard the 1,200-volume library of Americana of David B. Warden, who had been the United States consul at Paris. The Warden Library was particularly rich in French Americana.

In 1830 the Corporation appropriated funds for another library of Americana, that formed by the bookseller Obadiah Rich.

Just as more recent libraries in other parts of the country have often emphasized the history of the area in which they are located, so did Harvard concentrate initially on what was, in effect, its local history. Gradually, other parts of the world were covered, and, in keeping with the Library's need to serve an international university, one of the most recently acquired special collections consists of books in Manchu.

Boston 17th June 1818

Rev'd Docter Kirkland
Dear Sir
Having been informed some time since that the late Profess Ebeling of Hamburgh had left a very extensive & valuable library containing many volums maps & Charts peculiarly adapted to be usefull in the United States I determined upon purchasing it provided it could be obtained at a fair price considering its intrinsic worth & to present it to the University at Cambridge as a mark of the great esteem I feel for those who compose the government of that seminary & of veneration for its great Antiquity & usefulness. —— You will perceive by the inclosed letters & copies that this Object has been effected & that orders

On p. 2 of this letter presenting the Ebeling Collection, Israel Thorndike writes: "I have to request that your Corporation will be pleased to accept this library, with my best wishes that it may be found conducive to the great end we all have in view, the extension of knowledge in our country." Thorndike is one of the many benefactors of the Library, who, without formal connection to the University, was moved to generosity by the desire to extend knowledge.

The Library Expands
the Geographic Scope of the Collections

"Would it not be advisable, Sir, to take a *literary* journal from France, Germany, Italy, & perhaps from Spain? Would it not be well, also, to take one good Magazine? We now take none."

This short statement from Benjamin Peirce to President John T. Kirkland (undated, but apparently 1827) reveals much about the weakness of the Library. It also shows that Peirce, one of the first librarians to try to shape the Library, aspired to an international collection. Even with the limited resources available, steps had earlier been taken to satisfy this aspiration, and others would follow. George Ticknor had built up the holdings in the literatures of the Romance languages. His successor as the Smith Professor of Modern Languages, Henry Wadsworth Longfellow, did the same for the Scandinavian. Spending from an appropriation of $1,000, he shipped back 250 books from Stockholm in the summer of 1835, and in December of that year the librarian accessioned 400 books purchased by Longfellow in Copenhagen.

George Ticknor in 1828.
Before his purchases in Europe, "the only Spanish books [in the Library in 1817]
. . . of any importance" consisted of three titles. On pp. 58-59 are facing pages
of the accessions record for 1835, showing purchases of Ticknor's successor,
Henry Wadsworth Longfellow; some were made with his own funds.

Books received

Date.	Names.	No. of vols. Series
1835		
Decr 30.	Molbech, Christian. Forelæsninger over den nyere danske Poesie, fornemlig efter Digterne Evald, Baggesen og Oehlenschlägers Værker. Deel 1–2.	2 vol. 8vo.
"	Edda Sæmundar hinns Fröda: Exd: Rhythmica cum Antiquior, tales Sæmundina dicta; cum Interpretatione Latina, Lectionibus Variis, Notis, Glossario Vocum, et Indice Rerum.	3 vol. 4to.
"	Wolff, Otto. Greve Peder Griffenfields Levnet, et Bidrag til Danmarks Historie under Konge Christian den Femte.	1 vol. 4to.
"	Samling af Klub-Sange. [title page and 53]	1 vol. 12mo.
"	Molbech, Christian. Dansk poetisk Anthologie. Deel 1–2.	2 vols. 12mo.
"	Frorm, Benjamin Georg. Danskgyldige danske Ords Bemærkelser, oplyst ved Betragtninger og Exempler, udgivet i alphabetisk orden, med nogle faa Tillæg af Ludvig Heiberg.	1 vol. 8vo.
"	Schøning, Gerhard. Norges Riges Historie. Deel 1–3.	3 vols. 2. 4to.
"	Rask, K. Kortfattet Vejledning til det Oldnordiske eller gamle Islandske Sprog.	Fr. p.fr. 2. 8vo.
"	Mohr, N. Forsøg til en Islandsk Naturhistorie, med adskillige oeconomiske samt andre Anmærkninger.	1 vol. 8vo.
"	Rahbek, K. L. Dansk Læsebog og Exempelsamling til de lærde Skolers Brug. Bind 1–2.	2 vols. 2. 8vo.
"	Foersom, Peter. Digte. Deel 1–2.	2 vols. 8vo.
"	Bagger, Carl. Smaadigte.	Fr. p. 123. 2. 8vo.
"	——. Dronning Christine af Sverrig og Monaldeschi. Tragoedie. Fr. p. 97. 2. 8vo.
"	Rahbek, K. L. Om Ludvig Holberg som Lystspildigter og om hans Lystspil. Deel 1–3.	3 vols. 2. 8vo.
"	Visebog, Nyeste, af blandet Indhold.	1 vol. 2. 12mo.
"	Nielsen, Christian. De Gamle Vises Exempler oc Hof-Sprock.	1 vol. 16mo.
"	Baggesen, Jens Immanuel. Eventyrer og Comiske Fortællinger. Deel 1–2.	2 vols. 2. 8vo.
"	———————. Skiemtsomme Rümbreve.	1 vol. 2. 8vo.
"	———————. Giengangeren og han selv, eller Baggesen over Baggesen.	1 vol. 2. 8vo.
"	———————. Nye Blandede Digte.	1 vol. 2. 8vo.
"	Oehlenschläger, Adam Gottlob. Nyeste Blandede Digte.	1 vol. 2. 8vo.
"	———————. Nordiske Digte.	1 vol. 2. 8vo.
"	———————. Nye Poetiske Skrifter. Deel 1–3.	3 vols. square 8vo.
"	———————. Fiolna for Aaret 1812.	1 vol. 2. 12mo.
"	———————. Fiskeren.	1 vol. 2. 8vo.
"	———————. Hroars Saga.	1 vol. 2. 8vo.
"	———————. Robinson i England; Comedie.	1 vol. 2. 8vo.
"	———————. Freias Alter; Lystspil.	1 vol. 2. 8vo.
"	Baggesen, Jens Immanuel. Digtervandringer eller Reisen i Europa &. Første Deel.	1 vol. 2. 8vo.

Where printed.	When.	Of whom received.	Cost.	Condition.	Plates &c.	Class.
		Prof. H. W. Longfellow. Copenhagen.				
Kiöbenhavn.	1832.			Vol. 1st &c. 2 parts.		On B.
Hafnia.	787 – 1828.	do.		{ Vol 1. Sheep. / Vol 2. Boards. / Vol 3. Sheets.	1 vign. Tit. / 2 do. – do. / 1 vign. Tit. }	
Kiöbenhavn	1820.	do.		Boards.		
	1830 – 32.	do.		Half Sheep.		
Kiöbenhavn	1830 – 32.	do.		Boards.		
Kiöbenhavn	1807.	do.		Half Sheep.	1 Portrait & 1 vign. Tit.	
Norge & Kiöbenhavn.	1771 – 81.	do.		Sheep.	Vol 1. map.	
Kiöbenhavn	1832.	do.		Paper.		
Kiöben havn.	1788.	do.		Boards.	7 Plates.	
Kiöbenhavn.	1818 – 25.	do.		Half Calf.		
Kiöbenhavn.	1818.	do.		Boards.	2 col. portraits.	
Kjøbenhavn.	1834.	do.		Paper.		
Kjøbenhavn.	1833.	do.		do.		
Kjøbenhavn.	1815 – 17.	do.		Half Sheep.		
Kiöbenhavn.	1819.	do.		Half Calf.		
Kiöbenhavn.	1818.	do.		Sheep.		
Kiöbenhavn.	1807.	do.		Paper.		
Kiöbenhavn.	1807.	do.		do.		
Kiöbenhavn.	1807.	do.		do.		
Kiöbenhavn.	1807.	do.		do.		
Kiöbenhavn.	1808.	do.		do.		
Kiöbenhavn.	1807.	do.		Sheep.		
Kiöbenhavn.	1828 – 29.	do.		Half Calf.		
Kiöbenhavn.	1822.	do.		Boards.	Vign. Tit.	
[Kiöbenhavn.	1816?]	do.		do.		
Kiöbenhavn.	1817.	do.		do.		
Kiöbenhavn.	1819.	do.		Paper.		
Kiöbenhavn.	1816	do.		do.		
Kiöbenhavn.	1807.	do.		do.	Portrait.	

Harvard's Librarians Begin
to Act Professionally

I have been thinking for some time that I would say a word to you respecting my salary. . . .

It is not with me in one respect, as it has been, you know, with former Librarians; — my attention & time are *wholly* engrossed by the business of the office. . . . There is no office in the University, I am persuaded, in which the constant attention of one person of education is needed more than this. . . .

The above letter, dated 24 September 1827 and addressed to Dr. Nathaniel Bowditch, was drafted at a time of transition. For a century and a half, ever since Solomon Stoddard (class of 1662 who had taken his second degree in 1665) had been appointed Library Keeper in 1667, librarians had by custom been recent graduates. They opened the Library a few hours a week, charged out the books, reshelved them, and enforced the rules. They did not shape the collections and services.

Harvard made the transition from library keeper to policy-making librarian earlier than other colleges, though a precise date cannot be assigned. The change was evolutionary. Length of tenure suggests a change in the librarian's role but is not in itself conclusive. James Winthrop held the position from 1772 to 1787, but he seems to have initiated no policy discussions or changes, and short tenures followed his. Thaddeus Mason Harris, librarian from 1791 to 1793, was the first Harvard librarian to write a bibliothecal publication, *A Seleced* [sic] *Catalogue of Some of the Most Esteemed Publications in the English Language* (Boston, 1793), but the call of the ministry was too strong. His successor, Samuel Shapleigh, librarian from 1793 to 1800, was clearly devoted to the Library, as his will provided that a major portion of his estate establish a book fund, but his seven years in office were not ones with new developments.

In the nineteenth century, a definite change took place. Librarians began to urge change and to express their wishes in writing. Andrews Norton (1813–1821) wrote a 16-page "statement respecting the deficiencies of the Library" to the Corporation in 1818. Among his recommendations was that the office of librarian be made "a permanent one with a suitable salary." His successor, Joseph G. Cogswell (1821–1823), wrote a 13-page report on the arrangement of the Library in 1822. Charles Folsom (1823–1826) wrote to the President outlining the duties of the librarian and detailing the special tasks that needed to be undertaken. Benjamin Peirce (1826–1831), as noted, saw the job as completely engrossing.

Peirce died in 1831. The other men left for various reasons, among which was failure to get the support they desired. Thaddeus William Harris, who became librarian in 1831, stayed on until 1856. A sign of his role is that he started to write regular annual reports, apparently on his own initiative. He even acquired an assistant in 1841, John Langdon Sibley, who succeeded to the post of librarian and held it until retiring in 1877. His successor was Justin Winsor, a leader of the American Library Association. Thus, from 1831 Harvard had librarians who exerted leadership.

Four early Harvard librarians.
Left to right: Andrews Norton, Joseph G. Cogswell, Charles Folsom,
Thaddeus William Harris.

1828

The Map Collection Serves the Nation in a Boundary Dispute

The Harvard Map Collection helped shape the boundary between the United States and Canada. In 1828 the United States and Great Britain agreed to settle by arbitration a dispute over the northeastern boundary. At issue was a strip of land claimed by both New Brunswick and the state of Maine. The U.S. agents responsible for formulating this country's case turned to the Harvard Library for material that was unavailable elsewhere. The maps and books were loaned to the commissioners, and a compromise settlement, which was not unfavorable to this country, was reached.

Maps became an important part of the Library in 1818, when 10,000 were acquired as part of the Ebeling Library. The *Catalogue of the Maps and Charts*, published in 1831, is the first instance in which the Library disseminated information about a special collection.

The Library has continued to acquire great map collections, notably the Hauslab-Prince Liechtenstein collection of early maps and the Bagrow collection of Russian maps. But it emphasizes acquisition of currently published maps from around the world. Each map or map series is individually cataloged. That, plus the strength of the collection, make it an important resource for instruction in the classroom as well as research.

A large number of maps are also in the Geological Sciences Library.

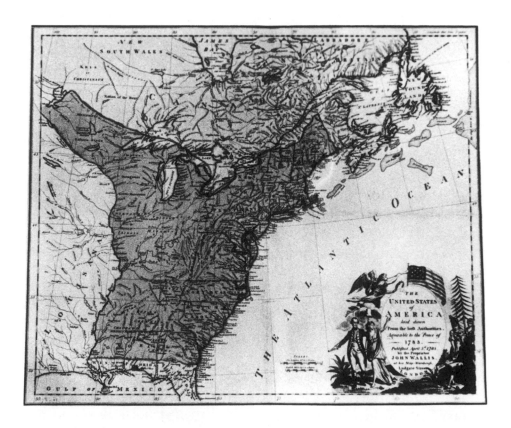

This map was one of the items loaned to the Government,
as is recorded on its back. The map is also the first to display the U.S. flag.
Harvard had difficulty in getting it back.

1828

Decentralization at Harvard
Is Not Always Easy

Librarian Benjamin Peirce wrote to Thomas Nuttall, curator of the Botanical Garden and librarian of the Natural History Library, 4 October 1828: "Sir It is was [sic] the wish of the Corporation that the Catalogue, they employed me to publish should comprehend all the books belonging to the *University*, whether in the public Library [the term often used at this period for the main library] of which I have charge, or in those libraries under the charge of others, viz. the Law, Theological, and Natural History libraries." In this draft letter Peirce went on to complain that he could not carry out his duty, because Nuttall had not allowed him to examine the books in the Natural History Library.

After also writing to the treasurer, who served as an administrative officer, Peirce received a brief reply from Nuttall: "If it would be convenient for you to examine the books any time to-day, during my absence in Boston, I will thank you, as I soon intend journeying from hence for some months and would rather you would manage the books before I went. . . ." Peirce noted on an inner page—obviously with anger — that he had received the note after one o'clock.

Several years later, on 19 January 1832, the records of the Corporation show that it received and put on file "the Librarian's receipt for 303 volumes from Mr. Nuttall, being part of the Natural History Library formerly in his charge."

The decentralized library system in which such a clash was possible began to form early in the nineteenth century. A separate medical library, established with the gift that Ward Nicholas Boylston had made to the College Library in 1800, was established in 1803, and shortly after 1816 the Medical School, which had moved to Boston,

Thomas Nuttall.

Catalogus Bibliotheca Institutionis Historia Naturalis Massachusettensis, sub manu et cura professoris.

I. *Historia Naturalis Miscella.*

Annales du Museum d'Histoire Naturelle 1802 à 1807	10 vols.	4to
Acta Litteraria Svecia ... 1720 à 1739	4	4^h
Nova Acta Academiæ Naturæ curiosorum 1757 à 1767	5	4to
Nova Commentaria Gottingensia ... 1771 à 1773	3	4to
Manchester Memoirs	5	8vo
Barteri Opuscula subseciva	1	4to
Redi experimenta naturalia	1	16mo
Existence De Dieu démontrée par les marveilles de la Nature	1	4to
Buchoz figures des animaux &c	1	fol.
Pisonis Historia Naturalis Brazilia	1	fol.
Seba Thesaurus Rerum naturalium	4	fol.
White's works on Natural History	2	8vo
Plinii Historia naturalis. Edit. Manutiana 1559.	1	fol. min.

This list of the books in the Natural History Library, prepared by Nuttall, was unsatisfactory, according to Peirce.

established its own library. The Divinity School had, at least as early as 1812, a library of duplicates from the College Library. The Law School, founded in 1817, had from its earliest days a library.

The Natural History Library disappears from the records after 1832, but at mid-century and shortly thereafter a number of scientific libraries were established. No decade since then has passed without other libraries coming into being. There are now nearly 100.

The Harvard Library is thus a federation of libraries in which "each tub is on its own bottom." "Coordinated decentralization" is the more elegant expression that Keyes Metcalf, director from 1937 to 1955, coined to describe its administrative functioning. The coordination is provided by the Director of the University Library, whose office is, symbolically, not in a library. With no books under his control, his position is an anomaly in the library world. Fortunately, a Peirce-Nuttall type of battle is usually also an anomaly at Harvard.

1839

The Library Issues Regulations
Generous for Their Time

The most famous story about the Library involves Librarian John Langdon Sibley and President Charles William Eliot. One day Eliot met Sibley walking across the Yard with a smile on his face and inquired where he was going. Sibley replied: "The Library is locked up and every book is in it but two, and I know where they are and I am going to get them." The story is no doubt essentially true (the year was probably 1858 when Eliot was still a tutor), but to see it as a symbol of a librarian delighting in having the books all locked up and unused is false. Sibley was doing exactly what was expected of him. It was an ancient practice that all of the books were to be in the Library at the time of the examination by the Visiting Committee.

The short hours in most libraries, particularly the times during which books could be borrowed, have also been seen as an attempt to keep readers and books apart. It is true that throughout most of the century librarians did not have the service orientation of more modern librarians, but, given the recitation system of instruction and the lack of research by the faculty, the need for longer hours did not exist. Harvard's regulations of 1839 and earlier seem to have met with general satisfaction and were, in fact, more generous than those of other libraries. Discontent emerged only in the 1850s. When it did, Sibley found himself under great pressure, for the Library was understaffed. In 1858 the staff consisted for the first time of three people: Sibley, the Assistant Librarian, and a clerk. Yet, accessions were over 6,000 titles. Books had to be cataloged and supplied to readers; records kept; letters written to donors; annual reports written, and so on.

Sibley did not, though, attend meetings. He rejected appointment to the Library Council, until in January 1877 the President informed him that he had been appointed. Seven months later he retired.

REGULATIONS

CONCERNING THE USE OF THE

PUBLIC LIBRARY OF HARVARD UNIVERSITY.

I. In term-time the Library will be open on the first four secular days of the week from 9 A. M. till 1, and from 2 P. M. till 4, and on Fridays from 9 A. M. till 1, except on the days of Public Fast and Thanksgiving, the day of Election, the Fourth of July, and the days of Public Exhibitions and the Dudleian Lecture — during the Exercises. In the Vacations the Librarian will attend to the delivery, return, and consultation of books every Monday, from 9 A. M. till noon. And no book shall be borrowed from the Library at any time without the knowledge and presence of the Librarian, or of the Sublibrarian, when there is one.

II. *Theological* and *Law Students*, and other authorized *Resident Graduates*, will apply for and return books in termtime on the above-named days, at 2 o'clock, P. M. : *Undergraduates* from noon till 1 o'clock ; the Seniors and Juniors on Mondays and Thursdays, the Sophomores on Tuesdays, and the Freshmen on Wednesdays.

III. No person shall, *ordinarily*, be allowed to have from the Library more than three volumes at the same time ; no *Student* shall keep any book belonging to it more than six weeks ; nor any other person more than three months.

IV. No person shall write in the books except the Librarian or one authorized so to do by him or the Corporation.

Every book shall be returned in good condition, regard being had to the necessary wear of it with careful usage. And if any person shall mutilate, injure, or lose a book borrowed from the Library, he shall make it good to the satisfaction of the Librarian and of the Corporation.

V. *Students* are not allowed to carry out of town books belonging to the Library, without special leave ; and all books borrowed by them must be returned on or before the Tuesday immediately preceding the Winter Vacation. Those who reside in Cambridge during any vacation are permitted to have books at the regular times.

VI. *Every person, without exception*, having books from the Library, shall return them in the month of June annually, as soon, at the latest, as the ninth Wednesday before Commencement ; and all the books shall be retained in the Library, from and after said ninth Wednesday, twenty-five days, for the Annual Examination.

VII. Persons sending for books are required to make, sign, and date a written order for them, and to insert therein the authors' names and the words of the title as they stand in the printed Catalogue, and the page where found in said catalogue.

The Regulations of 1839.

1840

Librarian Harris Innovates
by Creating a Card Catalog

Thaddeus William Harris urged in his 1840 annual report

That the Corporation should authorize a slip catalogue to be made, consisting of the title of every work in the library, on pieces of card 6½ inches long and 1½ inches wide; such catalogue being much wanted when books are arranged for the Annual Examinations [of the Visiting Committee] to indicate missing books, and would also be extremely useful in facilitating the re-arrangement of books in the new library, and would serve for various other useful purposes hereafter.

It is not known what the president responded to Harris's proposal — apparently the first reference to a card catalog in an American library — but a "slip catalogue" soon began. Although the date 1848 is usually given, several drawers of cards still exists, and in one are a number of cards with slips pasted on for books acquired in 1843, plus one for an 1842 acquisition. Sometime before 1850, the entries were written directly on the cards. The catalog begun by Harris continued in use by the staff until 1912.

The term "slip catalogue" suggests the origin of Harris's idea. It goes back to the work of William Croswell, an exceedingly unhappy man, who spent the last years of his life, while supported by the Overseers of the Poor of the City of Boston, writing and rewriting petitions that complained about, among other things, his ill treatment by Harvard. In 1812 he had been hired to produce a new printed catalog, and he began by cutting up the printed catalog of 1790 into slips. Then he recorded acquisitions since 1790 on sheets of paper that he cut into slips. Subsequently, the slips were classed by subject and mounted in blank volumes. President Kirkland, who had begun to fear that Croswell was turning the task into lifetime employment, finally discharged him in 1821, and the duty of producing a new printed catalog devolved on Librarian Joseph Green Cogswell.

70

Jackson Jno. Journey from India towards England in the year 1797. 4to Lond. 1799.

Jeffries 6 Voyages from Asia to America published by Captn J. Jeffries. 2d ed. 4to Lo. 1764.

Jordan ... Paris Spectator containing observations on the Parisian manners and customs at the beginning of the 19th century trd fr the French by the author 12mo 3 vols. Phil 1816.

Johnston Rob. Travels through part of the Russian Empire and the Country of Poland along the shores of the Baltic 4to Lo. 1815. Pl. coloured.

Kalm Pehr 12 Travels into N. America trd. by J. R. Forster 2n 2d ed. 2 vols. Lo. 1772.

Keysler John Geo 24 Travels through Germany Bohemia & Hungary Switzerland Italy & Lorrain 4 vols. 4to Lo. 1756.

Kolbenfer 41 Present State of the Cape of Good Hope trd fr the High German by Mr Medley. 2 vols. 8vo. Lo. 1738-1731. Pl

Kotzebue Aug. von 69 Travels fr. Berlin through Switzerland to Paris in the Y. 1804. Fr. the Germ. 12mo 3 vols. Lo. 1804.

La Hontan Baron 28 New Voyages to N. America ... and the Contests of the Fr. & Engl. chiefly in ... with Voyages to Portugal & Denmark in an App. fr. the Fr. 2 vols. 8vo. Lo 1703

Lande (M. de la) Voyage d'un Francois en Italie fait dans les années 1765 & 66, 8vo, 8 tom, Venise, 1769.
Les planches pour le meme, 4to.

Lassels (Rich.) The voyage of Italy, or a compleat journey through it. 12mo, Paris, 1670.
Laval (Pere ...) Louisiane, 4to, Paris, 1728.

Leland John Vid Hearne / Thomas in History of Great Britain and Ireland
Lewis Hist of Exped under Capt. Lewis & Clark to the Pacific Ocean by order of the American Government 2 vols. 8vo Phil 1814 Am Lib

A page from Croswell's catalog, showing both printed
and handwritten slips pasted down, plus entries written directly on the page.

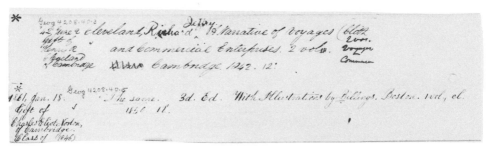

A drawer of the Harris catalog, plus a card with a slip pasted down.
Cards in the Harris catalog are 9 inches long.

Cogswell, later librarian of the Astor Library, one of the libraries that subsequently formed the New York Public Library, made much use of the Croswell catalog in rearranging books by subject. He also introduced an early form of the card catalog which he probably saw in German libraries. Each author's name was written at the head of a single sheet on which was noted the works of that author. Anonymous books were recorded alphabetically on sheets. Cogswell resigned in 1823 before completing the task, and his successor, Charles Folsom (1823–1826), copied the contents of the "sheet catalogue" into books. Benjamin Peirce subsequently used the "sheet catalogue" as printer's copy for the alphabetical portion of the 1830 printed catalog, after which it was "laid away in boxes."

Thaddeus William Harris, when he became librarian in 1831, would not have needed to consult the "sheet catalogue," but he would have referred from time to time to Croswell's earlier catalogs. Because they were created earlier, they would have helped to resolve some of the specific questions about holdings and shelfmarks that inevitably arise in day-to-day work in a library.

1841

The College Gets Its First
Separate Library Building

Gore Hall, opened in 1841, was the first building at Harvard to be used solely as a library. (The University of Virginia had built a library in 1825 but then also put it to a variety of uses; primacy in building a library that was used solely as a library goes to the University of South Carolina, 1840.)

To decrease the risk of fire, Gore Hall had only a tiny furnace. Harvard library users and staff, who had to wear hats and overcoats during the winter, were only slightly better off than those at Yale, Williams, and Amherst, where the libraries constructed in 1843, 1847, and 1853 had no furnaces. Because of inadequate heat and stone walls only one layer thick, green mold grew on some walls.

The books had to be read by natural light, for not until 1896 did Gore Hall have artificial light. The staff, for long even the head librarian, had no place to work except in open corridors. Sibley once complained that there was "not much more privacy than in the parlor, reading-room, or bar-room of a hotel."

The building was filled after twenty years. Alcoves were then divided, which meant that a book could not be gotten from a shelf without the individual working in the alcove having to move — both himself and his chair. By 1868 the Librarian was piling books on the floor. At one point the shelfmarks of all the books were changed to enable shelving by size, an enormous labor.

The addition of 1877, which contained six tiers of self-supporting iron stacks — their first use in an American library — temporarily provided adequate space for books, and the librarian also acquired an office. That no new functional building was then built can be seen only in retrospect as a blessing (for us, not those who suffered in Gore): a new building would certainly have been less adequate for the long run than the Widener building erected in 1915. It too, though, is now so crowded that working space and conditions have become a major problem.

Gore Hall before the addition of 1877.

Gore Hall with the addition of 1877.

The addition of 1877 contained six tiers of self-supporting stacks, as can be seen in this photo of the demolition of Gore Hall. Although this was their first use in the United States, such stacks had been installed in a European library in 1850.

The interior of Gore Hall, later subdivided into floors
in order to make possible a reading room.

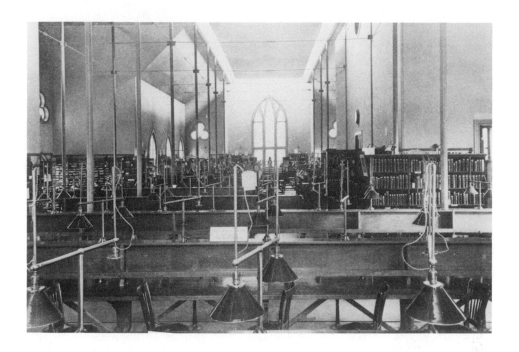

Above: The reading room on the top floor of Gore Hall about 1902;
below: The Delivery Room, or in modern terms the Circulation Desk,
on the ground floor of Gore Hall in 1912.

Harvard First Successfully Raises Funds
to Fill Gaps in the Collections

A fund-raising campaign for the Library was begun in December 1819, but it soon aborted. Rather than an official campaign undertaken with full support from the president and the Corporation, it may have been an effort by George Ticknor, who had taken up the Smith Professorship of French and Spanish Languages and Literatures in August 1819. Ticknor was certainly a strong advocate of the Library. While a student at Göttingen in 1816, he wrote to Stephen Higginson, the College Steward:

I cannot better explain to you the difference between our University in Cambridge and the one here than by telling you that here I hardly say too much when I say that it *consists* in the Library, and that in Cambridge the Library is one of the last things thought and talked about, — that here they have forty professors and more than two hundred thousand volumes to instruct them, and in Cambridge twenty professors and less than twenty thousand volumes. . . . We are mortified and exasperated because we have no learned men, and yet make it *physically* impossible for our scholars to become such. . . . You will, perhaps, say that these professors do not complain. I can only answer that you find the blind are often as gay and happy as those who are blessed with sight. . . .

Instead of turning to donors for funds, the Library tried to raise its own by the sale of duplicates, the major effort being concentrated between 1823 and 1828. Most of the books did not sell, although the Library of Congress and the University of Virginia, among other institutions and individuals, bought some of them.

The first successful campaign, known as the Donation Fund of 1842 or the Subscribed Fund of 1842, raised nearly $17,000. Instead of being set up as an endowment, the money was spent over the next few years. Once the money in the fund was gone, the Library returned, until 1859, to its normal state of poverty, with occasional and temporary relief by sales of duplicates.

Subscribers of $1000, and upwards.

The subscribers agree to pay the
sums annexed to their names
respectively for the purpose of
increasing the Library of
Harvard College. Octo. 1841.

Names.	Amount.
T H Perkins	One thousand Dollars
paid Wm Appleton	*paid* One thousand dollars
paid Sam & Appleton 26 May	One Thousand dollars
paid H Lowell *paid*	One thousand dollars
paid Joshua Bates by Mr Ward.	One thousand dollars
paid T W Ward	One thousand dollars
paid E Francis *paid May 19. 1842*	One Thousand Dollars
paid Abbott Lawrence	One Thousand Dollars
J P Cushing	One thousand dollars
paid John Wells	Two Thousand Dollars
paid N Appleton *paid*	One Thousand Dollars
paid David Sears *paid*	One thousand dollars
paid Jos. Peabody *paid*	One thousand Dollars
paid Geo. C. Shattuck *paid*	One thousand dollars

The page from the subscription book on which are recorded
donors of $1,000 or more to the Library in 1841 and 1842.

81

1849

An Undergraduate Uses the Library
of a Student Society

In the latter part of the eighteenth century students began to form clubs. Some primarily fostered conviviality; others offered educational opportunities not afforded by a curriculum based on daily recitations. Many of these student societies formed libraries, which flourished for much of the nineteenth century. Those students who were members often relied on the society libraries for a large proportion of the books that they read.

At Harvard the size of the student society libraries was relatively small compared to the central library. The Harvard College Library in 1849 had about 56,000 books, excluding pamphlets, and the student society libraries 12,000. This contrasts with Yale and many other colleges where the society libraries were larger than the college library, the figures for Yale in 1849 being 20,500 volumes in the college library and 27,500 in the student society libraries.

At Harvard the Adelphoi Theologia had 110 books in 1840; Hasty Pudding about 750 in 1841; the Institute of 1770 about 2,000 in 1849; the Natural History Society 125 in 1845; Phi Beta Kappa 230 in 1834; and the Porcellian about 4,000 in 1846. The Davy Club, a student scientific society, and the Pierian Sodality, a musical society, also had libraries, as did the Greek-letter fraternity A.D., which was "recognized" by the faculty in 1846. There may have been more.

Date	Horatio Alger Jr.	No. vol.	Shelf
Oct. 5	~~Sense & Sensibility~~	~~#~~	~~#~~
" 11	Yale Literary Magazine	~~#~~	~~#~~
" "	The Shrine	~~#~~	~~#~~
" "	Pacha of many Tales	~~#~~	~~#~~
" 15	Nuts to crack	1	~~19~~
" "	~~Kate Leslie~~ Aurungzebe	2	~~19~~
" 18	Roderick Random	1	2
" "	Cambridge Epitaph	1	~~54~~
Oct. 23	Peter Simple	1	~~12~~
Oct. 29	Japhet in search of a Father	1	~~14~~
" "	Humphrey Clinker	~~2~~	1
Nov 6	Pelham	2	13
" 12	Paul Clifford	2	12
" "	Am. Monthly Magazine	1	27
" 23	~~Randers~~	~~#~~	76
Dec 7	Eugene Aram	1	~~13~~
" "	Book of 101	~~#~~	~~18~~
Dec 10	Devereux	2	~~12~~
" 14	De Vere	2	2
" 17	Disowned	1	~~13~~
" 24	Nicholas Nickleby	2	~~16~~

Horatio Alger, Jr., read much fiction in the fall of 1849 from the holdings of the library of the Insititue of 1770.

1850

Harvard Begins to Organize Its Own
Records

At the urging of the American historian and Harvard president
Jared Sparks, the Corporation voted in 1850 that he "cause to be
examined and arranged all the manuscript papers relating to the
College . . . and procure such as are worthy of preservation to be
substantially bound." By 1900 the official Archives still occupied only
six locked iron cabinets, but much else had been acquired by fore-
sighted librarians. For instance, they always gratefully accepted the
classbooks, volumes maintained throughout life by class secretaries
about their classmates. These printed works and manuscripts, though
not official records, constitute an important part of the Archives.
Along with official records and ancillary material, the Archives now
also actively collects the personal papers of faculty and major administrative officers.

The University Archives serves a variety of purposes. It preserves
records because of their value to the University and makes them
available when needed for administrative reasons. It also helps to
control the quantity of records by advising on destruction. In 1982
a records manager was added to the staff to help in carrying out this
function. Yet the Archives is much more than a manager of records
for internal purposes. It is an extraordinary collection for research
on the history of American education and other aspects of American
life.

A part of the Library that manages, and even destroys, large quan-
tities of records for an organization with about 15,000 employees and
at the same time serves as curator of historical materials relating to
some of the most important figures in American life cannot present
a clear image. That may be why the importance of the Archives as
a historical resource is not, it seems, sufficiently understood either
within the University or the community of scholars.

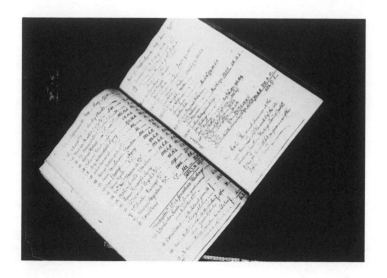

Above: The Treasurer's journal for 1777–1785 on Treasurer Ebenezer Storer's desk; *below*: Women in Lehman Hall in 1949-50 creating the type of records that the University Archives also manages.

John Langdon Sibley

John Langdon Sibley, class of 1825, was briefly an assistant in the Library in 1825–1826. Then he returned as assistant librarian in 1841 and served as librarian from 1856 until his retirement in 1877. Sibley was one of the first Americans to be able to devote his life to books and libraries.

Sibley's passion for the Harvard Library was both his great strength and his great weakness. He offended colleagues, professors, and college presidents by his inability to respect those who did not support his mighty passion. At the same time that intense inner light gave him a vision of a great library and the will to extraordinary efforts in its pursuit. "What is trash to me may be the part of the Library which will be the most valuable to another person," Sibley wrote in his private diary after being rebuked that the government documents he was begging only "lumbered up the Library."

In 1856 each graduate at the Commencement dinner found at his plate a circular asking for a copy of everything printed relating to America: "Daily applications from all parts of the United States are constantly revealing its [the Library's] poverty, and pressing upon its

HARVARD COLLEGE LIBRARY.

———

THE Libraries connected with Harvard College contain rather more than a hundred thousand volumes. About seventy thousand of these, and thirty thousand pamphlets, constitute the Public Library in Gore Hall. Most of them were given by their authors, or by friends of the University. Many of the works are very valuable, and some of the departments are well filled; but the permanent fund for the Library, as it yields but little more than three hundred dollars annually, does not allow an increase at all proportionate to the increasing wants of the officers and students, still less of the public. Daily applications from all parts of the United States are constantly revealing its poverty, and pressing upon its managers the importance of giving to it, as far as possible, a national character. It ought to contain at least one copy of every book, map, and pamphlet, written or published in this country, or pertaining to America.

As the Library is open for consultation to all visitors without charge, and is made as free as it can be consistently with the safe keeping and good treatment of its volumes, I take the liberty of expressing the pleasure I should have in placing on its shelves any volume or pamphlet of which any person who shall see this notice may be the author or publisher, and of inviting him to come and consult the Library on any subject in which he feels an interest.

JOHN LANGDON SIBLEY,
Librarian.

GORE HALL, July 16, 1856.

Each graduate at the Commencement dinner in 1856
received a copy of this circular.

87

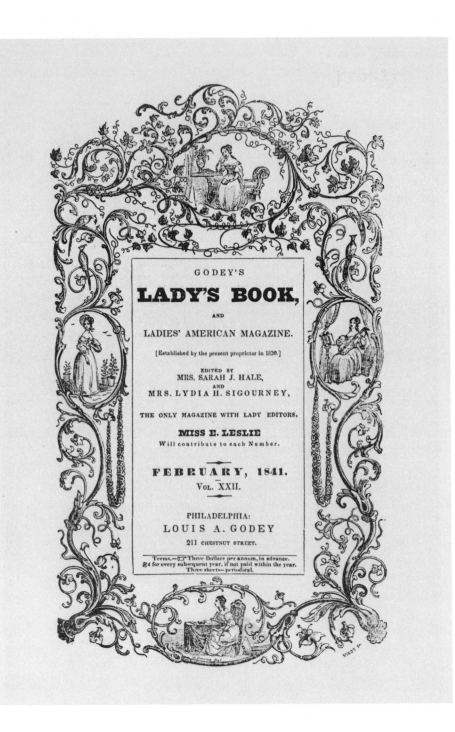

An issue of the periodical presented to the Library in 1842
at the urging of Sibley.

managers the importance of giving to it, as far as possible, a national character. It ought to contain at least one copy of every book, map, and pamphlet, written or published in this country, or pertaining to America."

Three years later, in a *Letter to the Committee of the Association of the Alumni Appointed to Take into Consideration the State of the College Library* (1859), Sibley expressed in print an expanded vision: "I think it would be well if it were generally known that there was never anything printed of which we should not be grateful for one copy."

Perhaps only the College Treasurer, Samuel A. Eliot, could handle Sibley's passion by joshing him. In a letter of 12 January 1847 he wrote: "If you will call at my office either tomorrow, Thursday, or Friday, I will show you a lot of some thirty pamphlets, very miscellaneous in date, subject & value, out of which you may select all you want for the College Library. Don't your mouth water?"

Sibley called at once on Eliot, and after the meeting on 13 January, Eliot wrote: "You are certainly the *most* omnivorous animal that has yet been created. I think you must be a distinct species." Sibley had even wanted almanacs.

During his tenure as assistant librarian, Sibley brought in by donation, he reckoned, 7,000 volumes and between 15,000 and 20,000 pamphlets. When he became librarian in 1856, the libraries of the University had about 100,000 volumes and pamphlets. At his retirement this figure had increased about fourfold.

Sibley's accomplishment must be counted in more than numbers. His desire for everything written helped make this Library a lode of source material as well as a collection of scholarly monographs. Imagine, if you will, the Exeter- and Harvard-educated, nearly middle-aged, bachelor Sibley meeting the editor of the *Lady's Book*, Sarah Josepha Hale. Of course, he turned suitor — for a gift of the periodical and her books. The meeting cannot be proven to have taken place, but the gift did; and it was clearly at Sibley's urging. He certainly knew that the publications had no immediate utility at Harvard, but that did not matter to Sibley. He was always thinking of the users in future generations. That attitude, Sibley's major legacy, has never been lost from sight.

1859

William Gray Provides Funds
for New Books

"There is nothing which has done so much to arrest inquiry, and discourage all attempts at the highest scholarship in this country, as the impossibility of obtaining the best works on every subject, wherever published, and as soon as published. This want you have provided the means of supplying." Thus began the letter of thanks that President James Walker wrote to William Gray on 28 February 1859. Gray, responding to appeals for book funds that had begun to be published in 1857, had just offered $5,000 a year for five years for books, with the wish that "the latest works be preferred to those of earlier date." His gift increased sixfold the funds available for books.

To oversee spending these funds, President Walker turned to the Library Committee, which had long existed, but added to its membership a secretary, the future president Charles William Eliot. Along with getting lists of desiderata from the faculty, Eliot sought advice from the Boston Public Library, after which he established an international network of agents to supply books.

Despite three essential steps toward modernization — funds to buy new books regularly, the more formal establishment of the means for selecting them, and the development of a systematic mechanism for acquiring them — the victory of the new was not complete in 1859. In 1860 the treasurer suggested that it would be wise to postpone further expenditure of Gray funds until the exchange rate was more favorable. Gray, in response, stated firmly that he wished the money to be spent whatever the exchange rate. In this conflict the actors were a cautious institutional money manager and a generous private donor, but the issue transcended personal approaches. At its heart were different conceptions of scholarship and the role of the Library, perhaps even of whether Harvard should be a research institution.

William Gray must quite consciously have shared President Walker's view that scholarship required comprehensive collecting of the best books upon their publication.

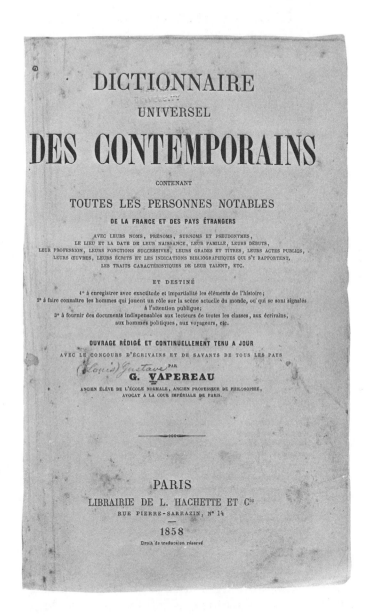

This biographical dictionary of contemporaries was the first book acquired with funds provided by William Gray.

1859

The Library Builds Collections
in Advance of Formal Instruction

When plans were drawn in 1859 to spend William Gray's gift for new books, the faculty Library Committee appropriated the funds as follows:

Theology and Oriental Languages and Literature	$300
American History	200
Zoology and geology	500
Greek	500
Latin	500
Botany	50
Philosophy and political economy	250
History, biography, and travels	600
Chemistry	600
Christian literature	50
Bibliography, criticism, and philology	600
Music	100
"Illustrations of the Fine Arts"	150
Rare Books	150
Natural philosophy	150

A course in part singing was first offered students in 1856; formal instruction in music began in 1871. Charles Eliot Norton started instruction in the fine arts in 1874. In both fields some library resources were clearly at hand. Indeed, acquisitions go back much beyond 1859.

Although relevant holdings continue to be housed in Widener and Houghton, both fields now have major libraries of their own. The Eda Kuhn Loeb Music Library opened in the fall of 1956, and the Fine Arts Library, housed in the Fogg and Sackler Museums, was established in 1962-63. In both cases material was moved from Widener, a step that also increased the available space.

THE
RUDIMENTS of MUSIC:
OR
A SHORT AND EASY TREATIS
ON THE
RULES of PSALMODY.
To which are annexed,
A NUMBER OF PLAIN TUNES AND CHANTS.
By *ANDREW LAW*, A. M.
AUTHOR OF SELECT HARMONY,
A Collection of plain Tunes for the Psalm Book, and a Collection of Hymn
Tunes, with their Hymns, lately published.
A. D. 1783.

*Library 10 Dec. 1783. Rec.ᵈ from the Author this & another
copy for which a rec.ᵗ is given of this date*
James Winthrop Lib.

The copy of Andrew Law's *Rudiments of Music* ([Cheshire, Conn.], 1783)
that was deposited in the Library to obtain copyright protection.

Above: Students using photographs in the Visual Collections for a class assignment in the 1940s; *below*: View across photograph cabinets today. Now photographs are used primarily for research, while slides, of which there are several hundred thousand, are more frequently used for instruction.

In both of these arts, important parts of the present collections were not initially developed by the Library. The Loeb Music Library has in its Isham Memorial Library a rich assemblage of early music in the original and, especially, in photostatic and microfilm reproductions; it began as a collection of organ music that was housed in a room near the organ in Memorial Church. Similarly, the Fine Arts Library has in its Visual Collections an extraordinary group of pictorial materials that began as a part of the Fogg Art Museum. These special collections, now thoroughly integrated into their respective libraries, help make them outstanding among university libraries in these fields. The Fine Arts Library also incorporates the 40,000 volumes that Fogg had begun to assemble in 1895.

The histories of these libraries are a further reminder that the Harvard Library owes part of its distinction to initiatives taken by individuals unconnected with the Library. The Harvard libraries, to be sure, get support from their rich parents, but they must, at the same time, compete for that support — and for access to possible support from outside — with faculty and administrators who have their own goals. Perhaps a recognition of that fact, plus an awareness of the importance of the Library to the University, has led to the Director being for most of this century a senior member of the faculty.

The basic rule at Harvard seems to have been — and may still be — that you can build what you want provided you can pay for it. And that means in most cases new funds.

The First American Card Catalog for Users Is Proposed

The first American card catalog created for public use was proposed in 1860 and begun in 1862. This simple but revolutionary step solved the problem of keeping the Library's public catalog up-to-date, but why did it take so long to turn to a card catalog for the public when one for the staff had existed since the 1840s? Some practical problems had first to be solved. Cabinets and drawers had to be designed so that the cards could be easily perused but not easily withdrawn and lost or gotten out of order, or totally scrambled when a drawer was dropped. Assistant Librarian Ezra Abbot's solutions to those problems, described in the Annual Report for the year 1863, were adopted throughout American libraries.

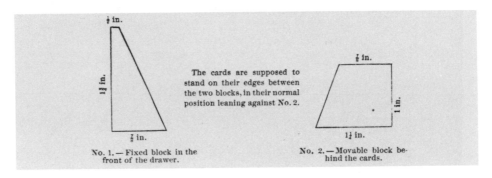

⅛ in.

1¼ in.

⅞ in.

The cards are supposed to stand on their edges between the two blocks, in their normal position leaning against No. 2.

⅞ in.

1 in.

1¼ in.

No. 1. — Fixed block in the
front of the drawer.

No. 2. — Movable block behind the cards.

Although not conceptually a leap, the card catalog did mean a loss that had to be accepted; the traditional book catalog that the scholar could have on nearby shelves was clearly being given up. It is probably not coincidental that Sibley proposed the card catalog in 1860, the year after Gray's gift for current acquisitions made it clear that a book catalog could not be up-to-date. He and Abbot had found the solution to keeping the catalog current.

They also made loss of the book catalog more palatable by improving subject access, and American libraries, in contrast with many of their European counterparts, are notable for having catalogs in which readers may look up books by subject. The original subject catalog was what came to be known as an alphabetico-classed catalog. Its divisions and subdivisions did not correspond to some ideal classification of knowledge. Instead, headings, chosen for practical reasons, were alphabetically arranged: Accidents, Acoustics, Aesthetics, Agriculture, etc. Each main heading was subdivided, with the subdivisions also arranged alphabetically under the main heading. Additional topical divisions could also be made. Since the books were not themselves classed by subject, this form of catalog was especially useful.

The timing of the transition to a new catalog probably reflects as well the availability of women to carry out the labor-intensive work at low pay. Following the example of the Boston Athenaeum, which had in 1857 become the first American library to hire women, Harvard did so in 1859. Sibley recorded the event in his journal under the date of 11 April 1859: "Began to employ female help in the Library. Miss Caroline Louisa & Miss Ellen Maria, daughters of the late Samuel Sawyer, M.D., of Cambridge (Class 1827) began copying lists of books to be bought, which have been brought in by Professors. Compensation six cents per hour for the present. Mr. Nelson 10 cents per hour." (Mr. Nelson's duties are not known.) On 11 June "young women began to assist in writing, cataloguing &c. in the Library." The "cataloguing" they did was not then for the public catalog. Work on that began in May 1862, with 35,762 cards written the first year.

A card from Abbot's subject catalog.

97

The Library Again Suffers
from Inadequate Book Funds

William Gray's $5,000 per year for five years, beginning in 1859, was not spent evenly, so it continued to affect the book budget up through 1864-65. But by 1865-66, the Gray money was totally gone, and the budget for books had dropped down to $1,134. This contrasted with the Boston Public Library, which spent in 1865 $13,030 for books, and with the Boston Athenaeum, which had nearly $7,000 for books. Harvard's library crisis was not over. Indeed, the *Harvard Advocate*, plus such national journals as the *Nation* and *Appleton's Journal*, began to point out the shortage of book funds. *Appleton's* wrote in its 5 March 1870 issue that the Library could no longer compete with the Library of Congress or the Astor Library and that it was surpassed as well in excellence of management and service.

Again, individuals came forward, and by the end of the 1870s the Library had received nearly $125,000 in new book funds; this time they were endowed. The first of them, the bequest of $60,000 by Charles Minot in 1870, was specifically for "new books." The following decade saw another increment of nearly $70,000. In addition, endowed funds for the general purposes of the Library increased by over $500,000 during the 1870s and 1880s.

The struggle for adequate book funds had been long. The first general appeal resulted in the Donation Fund of 1842. Once spent, fifteen years of dearth followed. The next general appeal, begun in 1857, resulted in $25,000 from William Gray and over $6,000 from the alumni at large. Once Gray's gift was spent, five or six years of relative dearth then followed. The struggle was ended by the establishment of permanent book funds, endowed by individuals who recognized that the Library could effectively serve students and scholars only if it could rely on a steady income for regular purchases.

HARVARD COLLEGE
LIBRARY

FROM THE BEQUEST OF

JOHN AMORY LOWELL

CLASS OF 1815

HARVARD COL
LIBRARY

FROM THE BEQUEST OF

CHARLES SUMNER

CLASS OF 1830

Senator from Massachusetts

FOR BOOKS RELATING TO
POLITICS AND FINE ARTS

HARVARD COLLEGE
LIBRARY

FROM THE BEQUEST OF

MRS. ANNE E. P. SEVER

OF BOSTON

Widow of Col. James Warren Sever

(Class of 1817)

Bookplates, in current use, of some of the funds, endowed in the 1870s and 1880s, that for the first time insured that the Library could regularly build the collection.

1866

A Library Devoted to Anthropology Begins

On 2 November 1866 Paul A. Chadbourne of Williams College presented to the newly founded Peabody Museum of American Archaeology and Ethnology its first book, a copy of one of the first books printed (1859) in Greenland. This gift was symbolic: the library devoted to anthropology went on to collect material in many languages; gifts plus exchanges with other institutions, have been especially vital to its development; and its well-being has become important to anthropologists everywhere, not just at Harvard.

For long the Museum Library was only a working collection, rarely added to by purchase. Then, in the 1890s the Museum became more of a research institution. A research library became ever more desirable, and in 1906 Professor Roland B. Dixon was appointed librarian. He obtained funds for acquisitions, developed a unique classification system, and began to make catalog entries for articles. Thanks to the detailed subject headings and thorough indexing of journals, it is nowhere as easy to do anthropological research as in the Tozzer Library. The journal indexing continues and is currently published as *Anthropological Literature*, a major tool for scholars.

In 1974, the Library moved into a new building, named after the anthropologist Alfred M. Tozzer, librarian from 1934 to 1954. Many find the Tozzer building to be their favorite Harvard library. An extraordinary house post ornament from the Kwakiutal Indians of British Columbia, which is mounted on a wall, must remind many a reader that the subject matter is the fascinating one of human beings. It must also remind readers of the connection between field research and artifacts and books. The formal connection between the Museum and the Library, however, no longer exists. The Library became officially a member of the Harvard College Library system in 1979, a sign of a counter-trend to the pattern of decentralization.

The Tozzer Library.

Justin Winsor

In a preliminary report to President C. W. Eliot for 1876-77, Justin Winsor stated the viewpoint that was to guide him as Librarian from 1877 to 1897: "Books may be accumulated and guarded, and the result is sometimes called a library: but if the books are made to help and spur men on in their own daily work, the library becomes a vital influence; the prison is turned into a workshop."

A librarian with such views was exactly the person Eliot wanted. When Eliot in 1873 had called the library "the heart of the University," he was not employing a cliché. He was describing an attitude to scholarship and books that was a necessary element in his transformation of Harvard into a university. No longer were Harvard classes moving in step through textbooks. Instructors such as Henry Adams were requiring that each student "shall use to the utmost possible extent the resources of the College Library."

Winsor, who had been librarian of the Boston Public Library, the foremost in the nation, took steps to make the "utmost extent" of use possible. He ceased to call in books for annual inventory or to close the Library for cleaning; he extended the reserve book system, established a policy for selectively admitting students to the stacks, instituted a simplified system for charging out books, and introduced interlibrary lending. To reduce crowding in Gore Hall and to bring books closer to students, he established department, laboratory, and classroom libraries. These measures were effective. In 1874-75 57 percent of the students used the Library; in 1879-80 77 percent did so, and by 1887 the figure was 90 percent.

Winsor's pioneering emphasis on the Library as a "workshop" was widely influential. Through his example, writings, and presidency of the American Library Association during its first ten years (1876-

1885), he helped make U.S. libraries notable for the degree to which they have sought to bring books and readers together.

Justin Winsor's office.

Justin Winsor

The Harvard Library Today

The Harvard University Library has over 11.1 million printed books, including one of the first produced from movable type, the Bible that Gutenberg printed in Mainz about 1455. These books range in geography and language from scrolls printed by monks in Tibet to the latest books about computers issued by publishers in Harvard Square.

Harvard's books are housed and cared for in nearly 100 library units. Some are specialized by subject, and some enable the scholar and student to go back to the original sources. Others, including libraries in the undergraduate Houses, make books present everywhere in the student environment.

The largest of Harvard's libraries is the Harry Elkins Widener Memorial Library. Under its roof are housed 3.2 million volumes. By tunnel and bridge it is connected to millions more books and manuscripts in underground stacks, the visible signs of which are Houghton, Lamont, and the entrance and sunken courtyard of Pusey.

The holdings in these and other Harvard libraries are tied together by catalogs, which were formerly maintained on cards, but are now issued on microfiche. Within two years scholars and students in dormitory rooms, studies, offices, and homes will have access to the catalog through personal computers.

PHOTOGRAPHS BY WILLIAM MERCER

Harvard-Yenching Library

The Harry Elkins Widener Memorial Room,
with the Gutenberg Bible in the foreground

Leverett House Library

Hilles Library, Radcliffe College

The Union Catalog, the Distributable Union Catalog (DUC), and HOLLIS

Widener, Houghton, and Pusey Libraries, as seen from Lamont

Tozzer Library

Winsor's Library Staff Worked
under Strict Control

Winsor may have turned the Harvard Library into an Eden for its users. For the Library's workers, here is how it was intended to be, according to Order no 1, dated 8 December 1877:

The Librarian in instituting this Book of Orders desires the staff to understand some of the principles of efficient administration, as he comprehends them.

His views may not be at variance with their own; but there is an advantage in an explicit statement of what he counsels and expects. He considers —

That the demands of the Library upon their time and attention should be paramount, during the hours in which it is open.

That no absences should take place without as far as practicable, consultation beforehand.

That the Library reserves the right at all times to control in its own interests the hours of its assistants.

That all work should be promptly and faithfully done to the end that the Library may acquire a good name in which all its servants may share.

That the time-record should show the hours of actual duty, not mere presence in the building, and that there should be no communication, one with another, except when both are by the record either on or off duty.

That the ladies of the Catalogue Department should refrain from going into parts of the building, where they are liable to be addressed, unless their duties require; and to this end, that examination of titles should be made in the long cards, as far as that will suffice.

That the assistants should see that their acquaintances do not get into the habit of calling upon them in library hours. Callers needing to see assistants should be seen in the Delivery Room and there are objections to having unknown persons enter, without escort, the stack.

That tattle and gossip are in the highest degree objectionable, and a disqualification for service.

That while we could not harshly prohibit the pleasant word that lightens labor, there are still times when conversation hazards the accuracy of work, which needs care and full attention; and that reliance can assuredly be placed upon the good sense of the service to obviate the necessity of specific items of interdiction. . . .

Winsor Issues an Early Library
and Bibliographical Publications Series

In 1878 Justin Winsor added brief bibliographies and catalogs to the contents of the quarterly *Bulletin* of new acquisitions, first issued in 1875; as a result, other libraries in this country and Europe began to request copies. Because the bibliographical articles were printed from stereotype plates, Winsor was able easily to have them reprinted. Thus began the series of *Bibliographical Contributions*. It predates the founding of the great bibliographical societies of the English-speaking world and marks an on-going commitment by the Library to disseminate information.

Published between 1878 and 1911, the complete series has sixty numbers. Other publications followed: *Harvard Library Notes*, 1920 to 1942, and the *Harvard Library Bulletin*, 1947 to 1960, and 1967 to the present day. Other series and journals, as well as separate publications, appear steadily.

The Library also works with publishers to disseminate bibliographical information. Notable recent examples are the catalogs of the Law School, the Fine Arts Library, and the Music Library (all in microfiche) and the *Chinese and Japanese Catalogs of the Harvard-Yenching Library* and the *Catalogue of Manuscripts in the Houghton Library* (book form).

Microform technology makes it possible to reproduce the texts of entire collections, and, the Library, working with commercial publishers, has also disseminated the texts of tens of thousands of volumes. The largest has been the microform publication of the Kress Library's holdings as part of the *Goldsmiths'-Kress Library of Economic Literature*; other major microform publications include *German and Austrian Drama* from the Houghton Library, the *History of Music* from the Houghton Library and the Loeb Music Library, and *Nineteenth-Century Legal Treatises* from the Law School Library.

Library of Harvard University.

BIBLIOGRAPHICAL CONTRIBUTIONS.

EDITED BY JUSTIN WINSOR,

LIBRARIAN.

No. 26.

THE CARLYLE COLLECTION.

A CATALOGUE OF BOOKS

ON

OLIVER CROMWELL AND FREDERICK THE GREAT

BEQUEATHED BY THOMAS CARLYLE TO HARVARD COLLEGE LIBRARY.

BY WILLIAM COOLIDGE LANE.

CAMBRIDGE, MASS.:

Issued by the Library of Harvard University.

1888.

An issue of *Bibliographical Contributions*.

Science Libraries Proliferate and Later Benefit from Coordination

The first major publication of the Harvard University Library, other than catalogs of holdings, was Samuel H. Scudder, *A Catalogue of Scientific Serials of All Countries, Including the Transactions of Learned Societies in the Natural, Physical and Mathematical Sciences, 1633–1876* (1879). Harvard holdings would have greatly assisted in its compilation, for they were then significant in science. The College Library had three book funds restricted to science, out of a total of nineteen: the Horace Appleton Haven Fund established in 1844 (the first book fund to have been established since Shapleigh's in 1801) was for books in astronomy and mathematics; the George Hayward Fund, 1864, was for "the purchase of books of modern science and literature"; and

the bequest of Eliza Farrar in 1871 was for "the purchase of books in the department of Mathematics, Astronomy, and Natural Philosophy."

Specialized scientific libraries had also proliferated. The first were libraries of institutions affiliated with the College: Lawrence Scientific School (1847, which was amalgamated with the Faculty of Arts and Sciences in 1890, Gordon McKay being its successor library), the Harvard College Observatory (1849, the Wolbach Library currently housing collections of the Harvard College Observatory and the Smithsonian Astrophysical Observatory), the Museum of Comparative Zoology (1859), Gray Herbarium (1864), Arnold Arbo-

Above: Searching a scientific database in the Cabot Science Library;
left: The Cabot Science Library in the Science Center.

109

A view of the Museum of Comparative Zoology Library with a bust of the founder, Louis Agassiz (1807–1873), and Audubon's *Wild Turkey Cock and Hen and Nine Chickens*, the gift of John Eliot Thayer, 1885, in 1946.

retum (1874), and the Lucien Howe Library of Ophthalmology (1876). The Medical School Library had preceded them all, having been established shortly after 1816.

The number of scientific libraries made Scudder's bibliography a particularly useful tool for Harvard scientists, but except for historical purposes its utility soon became limited. Along with a growth in the number of scientific periodicals, there was a large increase in the number of special scientific libraries at Harvard. Departmental and divisional libraries were first established in the 1880s: Blue Hill Meteorological Observatory Library (1885), Physics Research Library (1886), Chemistry Library (1890), and Mathematics Library (1890, now the Birkhoff Mathematical Library). Growth in numbers continued in the twentieth century: Atkins Garden & Research Library (1901), Economic Botany Library of Oakes Ames (1918), Farlow Reference Library of Cryptogamic Botany (1921), Oakes Ames Orchid Library (1939), and Harvard Black Rock Forest Library (1956), all affiliated libraries; Biological Laboratories Library (1932), and Statistics (1958), departmental libraries; and Geological Sciences, which was established as a departmental library in 1930 and became part of the College Library in 1984.

Harvard had built outstanding collections, both retrospective and current, but in the post-sputnik era, in 1961, a Committee on Science Concentration recognized that yet another science library was desirable. It would serve to expose students to the breadth of scientific literature and also to reduce demand on the specialized research libraries. The prospect of a science center library stimulated thought of coordinating the science libraries, for the boundaries of their collections both overlap and change. A Science Specialist in the Harvard University Library was appointed in 1966, with the idea that the individual would eventually also head the science center library, which, in fact, happened when the Cabot Science Library opened in 1973.

Harvard thus took a major step toward overcoming the drawbacks of its decentralized library system, by means of coordination. The decision was timely; along with bringing other benefits to science students, Cabot has enabled students to do their own on-line searching of scientific databases or to get assistance. Given the desire to coordinate the science libraries, it is not surprising that the first computerized union listing at Harvard was of science periodicals from seven libraries (*Current Journals in the Sciences*, 1965).

111

1881

The "Librarian of the University"
Makes An Attempt to Centralize

In 1880 the Harvard Corporation, which owns and (with the consent of the Overseers) governs the University, voted that no department except the Law School should purchase a book "unless through the Librarian of the University" and that all books acquired should be sent to the College Library for cataloging. In January 1881 Justin Winsor had the text of the vote printed and distributed. He also printed up detailed instructions about procedures.

Winsor's efforts to centralize the libraries had begun shortly before his appointment at Harvard, when he was a member of the Sub-committee on the Administration of the Library, newly formed by the Overseers' Committee to Visit the Library. The Sub-committee's report recommended "that the University should have in effect one library" and that the "departmental" libraries should be "dependencies of the central one." The vote of 1880 can be seen as a major effort toward that end; and although Winsor attempted to enforce the vote and even expand its applicability, it is clear that by 1910 most of the departmental libraries had either been exempted or were violating the vote.

The attempt to centralize had failed, and centralization ceased to be an issue. Thereafter, the numerous administrative changes that have taken place have resulted from efforts to find the best means of coordination, given the personalities and issues of the time, but central control of the libraries of the faculties has not been attempted. The largest faculty library, the Harvard College Library, has, however, added units that were formerly independent.

HARVARD UNIVERSITY.

The Librarian respectfully suggests the following method of concerted action between those having the care of books belonging to the several departments of the University and himself, in order to carry out the intention of the President and Fellows, in their order of Dec. 13, 1880: —

The usual order-slip (to be furnished by the College Library) to be filled out by the department ordering a book; to be signed by some one representing that department, " for [the department] "; and to be sent to the Librarian. If this slip is marked *Haste*, the order to be sent at once for a special return by mail or by some other expeditious method. If not so marked, the order to be sent forward at the usual intervals.

When the book is received at the College Library, the cost of it to be carried to an account under the head of the department ordering. The condition of this account can at any time be given to the department requesting it; and at the end of the financial year it will be given in due course to the Treasurer.

A seal to be put in the book showing it to belong to the department ordering it, and the date of receipt filled in on the seal. The form of book plate used in the College Library to be employed, and space to be left for the department officer to insert any name of donor either of book or of the money used in buying it.

An author's or main-entry card to be made and kept in the official catalogue of the College Library, so as to show to what department the book has been sent.

A similar main-entry as well as subject cards (if the latter are desired) to be made for the departmental library, and sent with the book to such department.

If the cards in present use at the departments differ in size from those used in the subject catalogue of the College Library (5 inches long × 2 inches high), the entries will be made on such cards (in present use), if a stock of them is sent to the College Library. It would be better, however, except for the economy of not discarding back work, to adopt the size, called standard among libraries, used in the College Library.

Books received by the departments as gifts to be sent to the College Library for the same treatment.

The department to give to the Librarian the list of the periodicals or serials which it wishes ordered. The entry of these accessions to be made in the College Library from such lists, and instructions to be given to the agent supplying them to send them directly to the department. Correspondence in case of failure to receive numbers or parts to be had by the department directly with the agent to save time, or through the Librarian if preferred. Seals will be sent to be placed in the *bound* volumes, when notification is given.

The Librarian desires to add that he shall welcome suggestions tending to make the service imposed on him by the Corporation conduce as far as possible to the best interests of the University.

JUSTIN WINSOR, *Librarian of the University.*

CAMBRIDGE, GORE HALL, Jan. 20, 1881.

When Winsor consulted the Treasurer about distributing copies of this circular, the Treasurer expressed the view that it was sufficient to have copies available for use when questions arose. Thus, Winsor's efforts to centralize the libraries of the University, though formally approved by vote of the Corporation, may not have been fully supported by the University's authorities.

113

A Russian Revolutionary
Assists the Library

One of the fathers of the Slavic collection was a president of the United States, John Quincy Adams. On several occasions when in Europe, and particularly when ambassador to Russia between 1809 and 1814, he acquired Slavic books for Harvard. Professor Francis James Child, who especially built up the folklore collection, was responsible for about a thousand of the Slavic titles here before the twentieth century. Another father of the collection was Ivan Panin, a *cum laude* graduate in the class of 1882, who served as the American correspondent for the revolutionary journal *Obshchee delo*, published in  Geneva from 1877 to 1890; on 19 November 1885 he was given library privileges "in consideration of occasional service which he may be asked to render in regard to cataloging of Slavic books."

Panin offered his collection of Russian revolutionary literature to Harvard on 20 March 1896, two years after Archibald Cary Coolidge began to teach the first course on Russian history, and one year after Coolidge had bought for Harvard 1,371 titles of Slavica, almost the entire contents of a catalog from Harrassowitz in Leipzig. The timing of Panin's gift suggests it may have been stimulated by these affirmations of interest in the Slavic countries.

Over the years, the Library has bought books at every opportunity, some of them most unusual. Coolidge, for instance, while liaison chief with the American Relief Administration that sought to relieve famine in 1921 and 1922, also bought books. The books on Russian art that he then acquired are particularly notable. Today, acquiring at every opportunity also means acting quickly, for books published in the Soviet Union do not long remain in print. A unique system of exchange relationships has strengthened collections with many titles that are rare and difficult to acquire. In addition, the collection has continued to be enriched by major gifts. Two notable examples are the Trotsky Archives, whose purchase was made possible by John W. Blodgett, Jr., '23, and the Kilgour Collection of Russian Belles-Lettres, the gift of Bayard L. Kilgour '27. Mr. Kilgour also acquired for Harvard books relating to other aspects of Russian civilization, among them a unique copy of a grammar issued from the first Russian press. In recent years friends of the Ukrainian collection have greatly expanded the holdings of Ukrainian books, both in Widener and the Ukrainian Research Institute Reference Library.

The holdings of the libraries of the University in Slavic languages are estimated at between 500,000 and 600,000 volumes, with additional hundreds of thousands in Western languages on topics relevant to Slavic studies.

Bookplates from the Kilgour Collection of Russian Belles-Lettres.
Many of the books are from royal libraries.

1893

A Specialized
Architectural Library Begins

The first course in the history of architecture was given in 1893-94, and by 1897 a Department of Architecture was formally established. As early as 1900, the department's library had diverse media, including a "large collection" of photographs. In 1902 it was moved to the newly erected architectural building, Robinson Hall.

Another strand of the present Frances Loeb Library goes back to the year 1900 when the first course in landscape architecture was taught in an American university. A department was formally organized in 1909, and a second library was established in Robinson Hall in 1911. In 1936 these two departments, plus that devoted to regional planning, became departments within the new School of Design.

Because space had been planned in 1900 with the idea that "the library shall be a strictly working one," a severe shortage developed. Parts of the collection eventually had to be stored elsewhere. Lack of space probably even encouraged small appropriations for books; in 1952 the book budget was less than $1,000, a quarter of the amount spent in 1900. (In 1984-85 over $108,000 was spent for library materials.) Space did not, however, inhibit the formation of collections to serve the special needs of the School: photographs, lantern slides, blueprints, manufacturers' catalogs, and an extraordinary file of clippings and pamphlets. Manuscripts are also now part of the Loeb Library, and it has a special Le Corbusier Collection.

The generosity of John L. Loeb '24, made possible excellent accommodations for the Library in the School's new Gund Hall in 1972. Rapid expansion has followed, aided by the transfer of some materials from Widener. Substantial rare book holdings continue to be available in Houghton, and related material exists as well in the Fine Arts Library. These further the work of the School. So do the Frances Loeb Library's holdings, perhaps above all the visual collections, aid other departments, for visual materials are becoming increasingly important in instruction and research in many different fields.

The Frances Loeb Library of the Graduate School of Design.

The Harvard Library
Loses Its Leading Faculty Supporter

Harvard faculty members, according to a survey by the Faculty of Arts and Sciences in 1985, consider the Library a major inducement in accepting a Harvard appointment, and after working here, they find that it exceeds their expectations. Many of its members have themselves helped make it such a resource. Several, as director, have guided the Library. Some have left valuable collections and given funds for books. Most have given counsel, particularly in the selection of material, for not until 1953-54 did a member of the Library staff have full-time responsibility for book selection. Members of the faculty have also been strong advocates for the Library in the councils of the University, at times vigorously upholding collecting policies in the face of those who urged a lowering of sights for the institution.

Preeminent among faculty supporters of the Library in the nineteenth century was Francis James Child, professor of English. At the time of his death in 1896 he was directing Library expenditures for English language and literatures, medieval literature, the Romance languages and literatures, Scandinavian literatures, and Slavic languages and literatures, plus, above all, folklore. He made the ballad collection unrivaled.

Child's power extended beyond his selecting books in a large number of fields. He was a member of the Library Committee that was re-formed in 1859 and was chosen its secretary in 1865. When the Library Committee was succeeded by the Library Council in 1867, he was again elected secretary, a post that he held until his death in September 1896. From 1864 to 1896, Child missed only four meetings.

Through his position he was able to shape the outcome among the competing claims for Library funds, especially book funds. He even

Caricatures of Francis James Child, drawn by colleague William James.

James Russell Lowell, another major supporter of the Library,
at Elmwood about 1865.

argued — successfully — for rare books. On 12 August 1878, he wrote to his close friend James Russell Lowell:

I keep an eye on all the books I think you would like, and as we can spend nigh 16000 a year now, one gets pretty much what he asks for. I am even proposing to the Council to buy 3500 dollars worth of Medlicott's books — including some really fine things in the way of old authors More, Erasmus, Spenser, Froissart etc. We surely ought to have first editions of all the poets, of all the great literary pieces since printing began. Our former poverty has made even the Council timid about buying rare books. If we dont we shall have to spend our money on a huge quantity of recent things which will be forgotten in twenty years.

The Library had earlier bought old books, and certainly the rare had been treasured. Child's letter is, however, remarkable for its fully conscious statement of the desirability of first editions in a university library.

President Eliot Proposes Storage of "Dead" Books

Throughout President Charles William Eliot's long tenure (1869–1909), keeping a roof over Harvard's books bedeviled him. Twice, valuable restricted funds had to be spent to provide additions to Gore Hall, and no donor could be found to provide a new building that would have to be replaced, it appeared, in a relatively short time.

In his Report for 1900-01 Eliot expounded more fully than before his thoughts on the space problem. He proposed that books be stored at three or four main points in the country, such as the Library of Congress, New York, and Chicago. At the request of College Librarian William C. Lane, the Corporation appointed a committee. Although its report made concessions to the principle of segregating certain books, it was clear that only a small proportion of the collection would generally be considered "dead." The committee reported "a remarkable unanimity of opinion" that separating "live" books from "dead" was "inconsistent with the interests of learning" if it implied "the destruction or removal of the so-called dead books, or even the storing of them in such a way that they are not both well classified and directly accessible to scholars."

Eliot dropped the idea of three or four centers. Had it gone into effect, American universities might then have followed the German pattern of keeping university libraries small and relying on interlibrary loan, a pattern whose deplorable consequences for research in the humanities have recently been spelled out in a study sponsored by the Forschungsgemeinschaft.

Eliot did not, however, give up the basic idea. He spoke before library groups; another committee was appointed; and Lane himself conceded that the "prospect of indefinite accumulation at an ever increasing rate can not be faced with equanimity." By his Report for 1904-05 Eliot was advocating that books "should be stored in a cheap fireproof building on cheap land within half a mile of the Yard, [where] a single attendant at the new building, supplied with a telephone, could easily meet all demands for the 'dead' books under his care by making two trips a day between the new storehouse and Gore Hall." In 1906 an addition was made to Gore. In 1912, three years after Eliot's retirement, the announcement came that Mrs. George D. Widener would build a splendid new building in the Yard. There the matter rested until 1942 when Director of the Library Keyes Metcalf built the New England Deposit Library, a storage library like that advocated by Eliot, except that it was not fireproof, and no longer is it on cheap land.

Despite the New England Deposit Library, no library in the world has more books accessible to readers on open shelves than does the Harvard Library. The new Harvard Depository will not change that. The central collections of the Harvard Library have also never undergone a systematic weeding, though proposals have surfaced from time to time, both before and after Eliot. It may well be that every library has sometimes made mistakes by discarding books or insufficiently protecting them; unbound pamphlets have not always fared well at the hands of staff and users. But Harvard has had an extraordinary record of retaining what it initially acquires, for it is generally recognized that books can take on new life.

1901

Portraits of Garrick Form the Nucleus
of a Great Theatre Collection

The Harvard Theatre Collection, the first performing arts research library, marks its beginnings from November 1901 when Professor George Pierce Baker and a group of alumni presented the Library with a collection of portraits of the eighteenth-century actor David Garrick. The gift was in memory of Justin Winsor who had devoted many years to the study of Garrick's life and career. The remarkable private collections of Robert Gould Shaw, presented in 1915, and Evert Jansen Wendell, in 1918, encompassed every type of theatrical document from the most immediate record of the event, the playbill, to prints, original designs and drawings, photographs, letters, manuscripts, promptbooks, sheet music, and reviews. These and subsequent gifts firmly established the Harvard Theatre Collection as a center for research on all aspects of the history of performance.

The Harvard Theatre Collection is truly international in scope, including major holdings both historical and modern on the dance, cinema, circus, and popular entertainment. Located since 1976 in Pusey Library, the Harvard Theatre Collection is used by Harvard students and faculty as well as by performing artists and scholars from all over the world.

Mʳ GARRICK.
in the Character of MACBETH. Act.2.

A print of Garrick as Macbeth,
one of the portraits that forms the nucleus of the Theatre Collection.

125

1908

The Divinity School Library
Increases Dramatically

The Divinity School Library began with duplicates that in 1812 were set aside for the use of the School's students. By 1852 the collection numbered only 3,495 volumes. When the School's first separate library was built in 1887, the collection, with 20,000 volumes, was still modest; and the first librarian to provide continuous service was not employed until 1889.

This history contrasts with that of the Andover Theological Seminary Library. From 1808 it had purchased books regularly, and earlier than the main Harvard Library, it had been guided by a librarian who gave many years of service. The Divinity School's ability to rely on the central collection had inhibited its own library development.

In 1908 these two libraries merged. The joint collection contained 100,000 volumes, and in Andover Hall, the new library building on Harvard grounds, there was space for 100,000 more. The Library grew slowly, until after World War II, when the Divinity School itself was rejuvenated, and the Library began a period of great expansion. Since then book holdings have increased significantly. Its collections are particularly strong in early Protestantism in Europe, New England theology, the free church tradition and the liberal movement in American theology, and Biblical studies. The Library has also developed a manuscript collection that houses major Unitarian and Universalist archives and the papers of Paul Tillich among others. Now with over 375,000 volumes, the Library has outgrown an earlier addition and needs more space.

Extensive theological holdings continue to be developed in Widener, but a division of responsibility has been worked out in detail. The major responsibility is with the Divinity School, and its library ranks among the foremost theological collections in the country.

The Andover-Harvard Theological Library. The addition of 1961 complements the Gothic of Andover Hall; it was designed to allow for the addition of two more floors, which are now needed.

1908

The Harvard Business School Library
Starts out in an Alcove

The Graduate School of Business Administration, formally established on 30 March 1908, began its library with a few books housed in an alcove in Gore Hall. In 1915, after five years of improvised space in Lawrence Hall, the Library moved to the top floor of Widener, sharing a reading room with students of classics. Books soon had to be placed in Widener corridors and basements of buildings. In 1927 the books were moved into the new Baker Library on the campus on the Boston side of the Charles River.

By then there were also manuscripts, for Arthur H. Cole, later librarian of the Business School, had, while a student in 1916, located the records of the Slater Mills and arranged for them to be transferred to the Business School Library. From this nucleus grew a great collection of business archives. Dean Wallace B. Donham (1919–1942), influenced by the Law School's case method of instruction, also emulated the Law School in fostering a great library. He himself guaranteed the note for the purchase of Herbert Somerton Foxwell's library of early economic literature, which was later to be the gift of Claude W. Kress. In the meantime the estate of Senator Nelson Aldrich had presented his 10,000-volume library on finance. Baker Library came to be considered the world's greatest collection on business.

The Library is again pioneering: it is probably the Harvard library most active in helping its clientele conduct research using machine-readable data files.

The Business School campus, with Baker Library at the center,
on the day of its dedication in June 1927.

1910

Archibald Cary Coolidge

Archibald Cary Coolidge (1866–1928), Director of the Harvard University Library from 1910 to 1928, exerted more influence over higher education in the United States than all but a handful of college presidents. It was Coolidge who, through his teaching and through building the Harvard Library, made American education international in scope. With his own funds, Coolidge bought major collections for the Library. He also personally helped finance regular acquisitions and cataloging. He urged relatives to give. He and his family set the pace, but others joined in. And the Coolidge influence stimulated many other gifts and purchases of similar collections in the years after his death. They include an Icelandic collection of 10,000 volumes presented in memory of William Henry Schofield and the almost unrivaled H. Nelson Gay Collection on the history of the Italian Risorgimento. Here is an incomplete list of some of the major acquisitions during the years of Coolidge's involvement with the Library:

1895, 1,371 titles of Slavica from a catalog of the Harrassowitz firm, the gift of A. C. Coolidge; 1898-99, 322 volumes relating to the history of Poland, the gift of A. C. Coolidge; 1898-99, $3,000 for books on the history of Turkey and the Eastern question, the gift of J. Randolph Coolidge (A. C. Coolidge's father), which paid for the library of M. Charles Schefer of Paris, 445 volumes; 1899, the library of Count Riant relating to the Crusades and the Latin East, 7,649 volumes and nearly 1,200 pamphlets, the gift of the Coolidges; 1900, the library of Lombardini of Sollein, a Slovak writer, plus other material, 123 volumes and 1,567 pamphlets, the gift of A. C. Coolidge; 1900-01, $3,750 from A. C. Coolidge for books relating to the history of Poland and other Slavic countries, and to the history of the Ottoman Empire, including 300 *Zeitungen* or contemporary accounts

130

Archibald Cary Coolidge at work in Gore Hall.

From the Fernando Palha Collection,
acquired for Harvard in 1926 by Coolidge's friend, John B. Stetson, Jr.

132

Eltbůch:ſpiegel
vnd bildeniß des gantzen
erdtbodens von Sebaſtiano Franco
Wördēſi in vier bůcher/nemlich in Aſi
am/Aphricã/Europam/vnd America/gſtelt vnd abteilt/Auch aller darin be
griffner Länder/nation/Prouintzē vnd Inſeln/gelegenheit/gröſſe/weite/ge
wáchß/eygenſchafft/vnd der darinn gelegener völcker vnd einwoner/nam
men/geſtalt/leben/weſen/religion/glauben/ceremonien/gſatz/regimēt/
pollicey/ſitten/brauch/krieg/gewerb/frücht/thier/kleydung vñ ver
enderung/eygentlich für die augen geſtelt/Auch etwas võ new
gefundenen welten vnd Inſeln/nitt auß Beroſo/Joanne
de monte villa/S.Brandons Hiſtori/vñ dergleichen
fabeln/ſunð auß angenůmnen/glaubwirdigen
erfarnē/weltſchreibern/můſelig zůhauff tra
gē vñ auß vilen/weitleüffigen bůchern in
ein handtbůch eingeleibt vnd ver
faßt/vormals dergleichen
in Teütſch nie auß
gangen.

Mit einem zů end angehenckten Regiſter alles innhalts.

Kumpt her/vnd ſchauwet die werck des Herren/der ſo wunderbar
lich iſt/über die menſchen kinder.Pſal.xlvj.lxiiij.

ANNO. M. D. XXXIIII.

The *Weltbuch* of Sebastian Franck.
This description of the world may be seen as symbolic of Coolidge's gifts.

133

of the Turkish wars in the seventeenth century; 1901-02, Russian Nihilist pamphlets published in Geneva, the 100-volume set of *Russkaya Starina*, the 56-volume set of *Monumenta Hungariae historica*, the gift of A. C. Coolidge; 1902-03, a number of incunabula plus 30 early seventeenth-century Spanish pamphlets relating to Turkish affairs, the gift of A. C. Coolidge; 1903, a pledge of A. C. Coolidge to purchase 10,000 volumes on German history; 1903-04, the library of Konrad von Maurer of Old Norse law and Scandinavian history and literature, 10,000 volumes, the gift of A. C. Coolidge; 1906, $1,000 from A. C. Coolidge for books on French history; 1910, the Marshall C. Lefferts collection of Alexander Pope, 387 volumes and 128 pamphlets, the gift of J. P. Morgan, Jr., and others; 1912, the Marquis de Olivart collection of international law, 7,000 titles, acquired by the Law School but with Coolidge as the driving force; 1912, 175 Italian *statuti* and a library of criminology, which Coolidge arranged to be acquired by the Law School; 1913, several Latin American collections, the gift of A. C. Coolidge; 1913-1917, 1,000 volumes of Western Americana, the gift of Alice Forbes Perkins Hooper; 1915, Harry Elkins Widener Library, 3,000 volumes; 1915, the theatrical library of Robert Gould Shaw; 1916, Frederick Lewis Gay collection of British and American political tracts, 6,000 titles; 1916, English local history and topography, 1,700 volumes, acquired with a subscription fund; 1918, the theatrical library of Evert Jansen Wendell, 35,000 volumes and 2 million other pieces; 1920s, numerous gifts of James Buell Munn, including works by Milton and seventeenth-century English plays and poetry; 1925-26, Amy Lowell library, including a great Keats collection; 1925-26, widely diverse collections but of such quality and quantity that Coolidge wrote that the new acquisitions "alone would constitute one of the notable libraries in America"; 1926, Marietta Greenough collection of books on cooking and household management, 1,000 volumes; 1926, Fernando Palha library of Portuguese history and literature, 6,700 volumes, the gift of John B. Stetson, Jr.; 1927, Boulay de la Meurthe library on the French Revolution, 10,000 volumes and 30,000 pamphlets; 1927, a Ronsard collection.

Harvard's Desperate Need
for a New Library Is Well-Known

HARVARD COLLEGE LIBRARY CLIPPING SHEET

PLEASE GIVE HARVARD A LIBRARY BUILDING

Her Priceless Volumes Are Now Held in 73-Year-Old Antiquated House.

WANTED—A MILLIONAIRE.

Will some kind millionaire please give Harvard University a library building? Tainted money not barred. Mr. Rockefeller, take notice. Mr. Carnegie, please write.

Harvard University,
Cambridge, Mass.

When Harvard University finally unbends from its dignified aloofness and takes unto itself a press agent—as the university is now thinking of doing—his first job will be to separate some millionaire from several hundred thousands of dollars to build Harvard a library building. This is the one big need at Harvard. A happier man than President Lowell you would not be able to find in America this coming June if he could rise before the members of the Alumni Association at their annual meeting and say:

"Gentlemen, I am happy to tell you that we have been given $500,000 for a new library building from Mr. ———."

Now, if Harvard were in the circus business the job would be easy, and the task would be completed by coming Commencement Day. Imagine a scene like this, if Harvard were run along modern publicity lines, with a busy press agent to trumpet its wants to the world:

President—Boy, send for Mr. Jinks.

Mr. Jinks—Yes, sir.

President—Jinks, old boy, we need a library. Go out and find some millionaire and take the money away from him. Now, of course, use all those modern methods, but try to be dignified, if you can, but—get the library.

Mr. Jinks—Aye aye, sir.

Mr. Jinks then gets busy and sends out letters to millionaires somewhat in this manner, and with much black type:

DO YOU KNOW YOU ARE GOING TO DIE?

Well, you are. And do you want your name to go down into history as the man who got rich by selling Snoofer's Soap or Giggler's Ginger Ale?

Of course you don't. Well, here's a chance to get in right with posterity.

GIVE HARVARD A LIBRARY.

Think of a beautiful marble building situated among the green trees in Harvard yard, bearing over the door:

GIVEN BY JAMES WHIFFLETREE SNOOFER.

Think of the millions of young men who will bless your name!

Get your application in early!

Alas and alack, this method is for the future. Harvard has no press agent, and these means are out of the question for a hundred years or so. In the meantime, seriously, the University needs a library building.

America's oldest university has one of the world's finest libraries, owning 1,425,891 volumes. And to house this great collection of priceless books it has a library building—Gore Hall—which would be a disgrace to Podunkville-on-the-Kaw. There is not a town of 30,000 people in the United States which has not a better library building than Harvard University. The building is seventy-three years old.

Only a few of the books can be kept in the old, ugly, gray stone library building and journals are kept in 40 small libraries in various University buildings. Here is what Professor Archibald Cary Coolidge, chairman of the Library Council, says of the situation:

"Above all looms the necessity of a new library building. This has been pointed out so often that there is little for me to say on the subject except the obvious truism that every year makes the situation worse. With what is in many ways the finest collection of books in the country, we have the one in every way the worst housed, considering its value. As is well known, the building is far from safe, yet any loss from fire would be irreparable. It is crammed with books from top to bottom, and we have had to store some forty-five thousand of the volumes least called for in the cellars of Perkins, Walter Hastings and Robinson Halls, and in the Divinity School, where they still have to be reached somehow or other, for they continue to be in demand. Every year this vexatious and costly operation of sending thousands of our books outside must be continued with increasing discomfort until we get a new building."

Forty-five thousand books stored in cellars! Please note.

Charles Francis Adams, 2d, treasurer of the university, joins in this Macedonian cry for a new library, saying:

"Harvard needs a new library. The building we have is outgrown. We look forward to the time when we shall have a bigger one. It is not now contemplated and may not be until the funds are in sight. I don't know what a new library would cost. We have plans that would enable us to build onto the present library, in sections, and according to our means. A library gift would indeed be very acceptable to Harvard at this time."

Now, won't Mr. Carnegie crown his library-giving life with the finest library gift of all—a half-million dollar library building—to Harvard?

The *Boston American*, certainly not a mouthpiece of the Harvard administration, had some fun in this story on Harvard's need for a new Library.

1912

Mrs. Widener Gives Harvard, As a Memorial to Her Son, a Great New Library

In 1912 tragedy struck the Widener family: Harry Elkins Widener and his father both died when the *Titanic* struck an iceberg and sank.

Only twenty-seven at the time of his death but already known as an exceptionally knowledgeable book collector, Harry Widener left his collection to his mother with the request that it be given to Harvard when it could be provided with proper accommodation. As Harry Widener, class of 1907, knew from his undergraduate days, no such accommodation existed. Eleanor Elkins Widener considered various options for proper housing — a wing added to Gore Hall or a new, small building just for Harry's collection — but settled on a new library to be known as the Harry Elkins Widener Memorial Library. Her son's books are housed in the central rooms of the library, under the rotunda.

To the original collection, the Widener family subsequently added a copy of the Gutenberg Bible, the book that symbolizes the revolution in communications brought about by the invention of printing from movable type.

For many, this building, housing so many of the products resulting from that invention, symbolizes Harvard and its purposes.

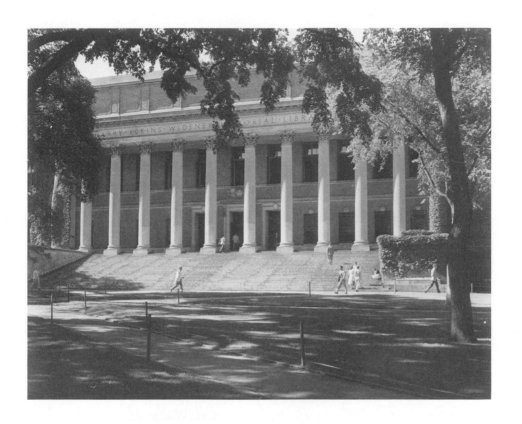

The Harry Elkins Widener Memorial Library.

Randall Hall was one of many locations that housed books from Gore Hall
while Widener Library was being built.
Randall stood on the site now occupied by William James Hall.

The stacks in Randall Hall.

Excavating for Widener Library.

Part of the stacks of Widener under construction.

1914

The First Independent Library Survey
Is Undertaken

In his Report for 1914, when Widener was under construction, Archibald Cary Coolidge expressed the belief that "the present time [is] the obvious one . . . for getting into as good condition as possible in order to begin life in the new building with a really efficient system of administration." The result was a survey of the Library by two students of the Graduate School of Business Administration, apparently the first U.S. library survey conducted by independent experts.

They particularly looked into cataloging and acquisition processes. Not unpredictably, the Librarian of the College, William C. Lane, felt that the inclusion of certain costs was "less useful in the case of a library than . . . in the case of a business house." One can thus see expressed the inevitable and continuing tension — present in the University administration, the faculty, and library administrators and library staff alike — between different concepts of where efficiency should dominate and where excellence in serving scholarly needs should be the foremost goal.

Historically, the desire for excellence has centered on the collection itself. In cataloging the desire for efficiency has dominated, for Harvard's cataloging records have traditionally been brief with relatively few subject headings. Acquiring the books and then getting them onto the shelves efficiently have both had much higher priority than helping people to use them. Winsor acted to extend use, and the Library has a tradition of distinguished exhibitions and publications that disseminate information on the collections; but to provide reference as an organized, staff function has generally been seen as not nearly so effective as letting students learn for themselves.

The Business School students, however, recommended the creation of a Reference Department. Although this suggestion was adopted, Widener provided minimal reference services until the late 1930s.

The Harry Elkins Widener
Memorial Library

The interior arrangement of the Widener Library — a grand stair leading to a reading room stretching across the front of the building — follows the pattern set by the Boston Public Library in 1895. It is the pattern adopted by American libraries until after the Second World War. The earliest libraries were like Gore: Gothic with a main hall having alcoves on the sides. Subsequently, after stacks became common, libraries tended to have a large reading room on the entrance level, either straight ahead or off to one side.

In Widener the books are stored on ten levels of load-bearing stacks built around two interior courtyards. Two of the stack levels are not visible from outside the building. The bottom level connects by tunnels with the Houghton Library, which has two levels of stacks below ground; with the Lamont Library, which also has two levels of stacks below ground (one of which houses Houghton books); and with the Pusey Library, whose three levels are below ground, two of them being stacks. Between the Pusey stacks and Lamont is another area that also houses Houghton material.

The imposing Widener building is a visible sign of the millions of books and manuscripts stored underground.

The Widener Reading Room in the Library's early years.
The ceiling then had skylights.

A 1960 cartoon by Dahl about Harvard's underground libraries.

1916

The Library Experiments
with a Recreational Reading Room

The Widener building had for a short time more than adequate space, which permitted the experiment known as the Farnsworth Room, whose aim was primarily "to have on its shelves such books as shall lay the foundation of literary culture and aid in forming the reading habit." No other university library had such a reading room and no one knew whether it would be used. Undergraduates did, indeed, read for pleasure in the Farnsworth Room. In fact, they were asked to leave if they were found using the comfortable chairs for course reading. By 1931 the Room that began as an experiment had served as a model for more than twenty-five similar rooms in college and public libraries in the United States and Canada. Repeated requests for a list of the books on its shelves led to printing the catalog in 1931.

The Farnsworth Room, a memorial to Henry Weston Farnsworth of the class of 1912, is now located in Lamont Library, a whole building designed to provide comfortable quarters for undergraduates. Moreover, the Houses in which students live after their freshman year also have libraries with a particularly pleasant atmosphere. These changed circumstances have enabled the Curator of the Woodberry Poetry Room, who is also in charge of the Farnsworth Room, to adapt the collection to fill a particular niche in the Harvard Library system. The Farnsworth Room collection now emphasizes prose works of poets, avant-garde fiction either written in English or translated into English, and literature by and about ethnic minorities in the United States.

Farnsworth Room in 1916.

1925

Coolidge Starts the First
Friends of the Library Group

Dec. 18 [1841] The reason offered why the legislature should not give money to Harvard College to build their Library, was that Harvard had so much already. But that is the very reason why it should have more: that certainly is its strongest claim at this moment. If I have a valuable antique in my possession, I should not give it to a stage driver, but to some collector who had already a cabinet . . . for then it would be sure to be seen by the greatest number of those whom it concerned.
— Manuscript journal of Ralph Waldo Emerson

The greatness of the Harvard Library has resulted to a considerable extent from the generosity of its friends. Many individuals have given great collections, and the Library has also depended heavily on friends for funds to purchase special collections and individual items of distinction. A Friends organization is, however, quite modern in date. Stimulated by the example of the Fogg Art Museum, which had organized a Friends group in 1913, and urged on by a number of the Library's supporters (above all Edgar Huidekoper Wells, then a leading rare book specialist in New York), Archibald Cary Coolidge formally established the Friends of the Library in April 1925. This was the first such organization in a university.

In 1927, the John Barnard Associates, an organization of similar type but without formal ties to the Library, was established. Its first object was "to honor the memory of John Barnard, who loved books and did what he could for Harvard." John Barnard, class of 1700, minister of the First Church in Marblehead, had given some particularly useful books after the fire of 1764 and had bequeathed £200 in 1770.

The Friends of the Harvard College Library continues to give an opportunity to individuals who love learning to do what they can for Harvard.

THE JOHN BARNARD ASSOCIATES

No. 1   June 15, 1927

The Executive Committee proposes to issue an invitation to join the Associates to:

Paul J. Sachs, '00
William Warren Smith, Jr., '23
Bradley Fisk, '26
Varian M. Fry, '30
Carlton Sprague Smith, '27

* * *

At the meeting on June 11, at Mr. Winship's farm in Charles River, two non-resident members were selected:
Gustave Pabst, Jr., '21, of the Embassy Staff at Berlin
Alfred Reginald Allen, '26, of Philadelphia

* * *

There was an informal gathering at the new home of the Dunster House Book Shop, on Monday evening, June 13. This was a house warming and christening of the cupboard set aside by Mr. Firuski for keeping records and other property of the Associates.

* * *

The members who will be in Cambridge during the Summer School, are planning to lunch together on Fridays.

* * *

Not quite half ($115) of the amount desired for the purchase of the Amy Lowell manuscript has been contributed by five members.

Checks may be sent to Mr. Wieser.

* * *

The dues for resident members are $5. Some members have not yet paid.

* * *

The Club Book, which Bruce Rogers is printing at the Harvard University Press, is ready to print, and ought to be finished this month.

There will be a special assessment of $10, to pay for this book, from present members. New members will receive the book upon payment of an initiation fee of $10.

There will be no copies for sale to non-members.

* * *

Please make all checks payable to the John Barnard Associates.

ELLIOT A. WIESER
Clerk

42 Apley Court
Cambridge, Mass.

The first publication of the John Barnard Associates.

149

1927

Harvard Begins to Influence East Asian Librarianship in the West

As recently as 1927 the Library's holdings in Chinese and Japanese amounted to little more than 6,000 volumes, and the sole course on the Far East was given only occasionally by Archibald Cary Coolidge. To Coolidge this was a situation that had to be remedied. In 1923 he obtained an anonymous fund to support a lectureship in the history of the Far East for five years. Then a few years later came the big opportunity. The trustees of a fund established under the will of Charles M. Hall, the discoverer of the first commercially successful process for making aluminum, decided, with the encouragement of Coolidge and Dean Wallace B. Donham of the Harvard Business School, to create a center for Far Eastern studies at Harvard. Even before the Harvard-Yenching Institute was established, Coolidge persuaded the trustees to make available funds for books and the salary of a librarian. Dr. A. Kaiming Chiu (1898–1977) was appointed to create a collection where almost none existed.

Dr. Chiu succeeded. A pioneer by temperament, he also created for the books that he was adding a classification scheme that was widely adopted. Along with solving problems inherent in cataloging books in Asian scripts, he made catalog cards available to other libraries. Thus, both through the example of his accomplishments at Harvard (he retired in 1965) and his advocacy of cooperative activities, Dr. Chiu exerted a major influence on East Asian librarianship in the West.

Now, with more than 655,000 volumes, the Harvard-Yenching Library is one of the greatest collections of East Asian material in the Western world.

A. Kaiming Chiu.

1930

Widener Introduces Security Checks

On 23 September 1930 a new rule took effect: everyone leaving the Widener building would have to submit "books, book-bags, brief-cases and the like for inspection." An inspection desk with a turnstile was installed, a Harvard innovation that has been taken up by virtually all academic libraries. Opposition to inspection was anticipated, but the arrest in 1931 of a ring of professional book thieves, who had stolen from Widener and other libraries, must have affirmed the decision.

The first recorded theft from the Harvard Library occurred in 1735. On 11 October of that year Andrew Boardman, 1737, son of the College Steward, was fined for stealing a library book.

> This book was stolen from Harvard College Library. It was later recovered. The thief was sentenced to two years at hard labor.
> 1932

In the middle of the nineteenth century Sibley opposed pressure for greater access to the books by pointing out, in his report for 1857, that "thirty-seven volumes have been abstracted from Gore Hall." The long-term trend was, however, toward greater access, and the trend was reinforced by the impossibility of taking regular inventories which would have revealed precise, and perhaps shocking, figures on losses. The turnstile probably resulted from a general impression, supported only by a sampling. Although the turnstile was removed in 1950, inspection desks continued, as has the search for means to tighten security without hampering or discouraging use.

The turnstile in Widener in 1930.

1931

Woodberry Poetry Room

Opened on 26 May 1931, thanks to a gift from Harry Harkness Flagler in memory of Professor George Edward Woodberry, the Poetry Room was one of the warmest and most welcoming spots in Widener. Although readings by poets, funded by Morris Gray, were initially for an invited audience, from 1934 they were administered by the English Department and given as much publicity as possible.

When the Woodberry Poetry Room moved to Lamont, it was into a room designed and furnished by Alvar and Aino Aalto, who took into account that the room's holdings included books and a collection of recorded readings. The first of the 2,000 recorded readings now held was by T. S. Eliot of the Harvard class of 1910; many of them have been published as records or cassettes. Among the recordings are the entire recorded archives of the Academy of American Poets, which have been remastered in the Poetry Room's own sound studio. A videotape collection is also now a part of the Room's holdings and includes tapes of some of the readings and related lectures given in the Room as part of the Lamont Poetry Reading Series, begun in 1977.

Notable for its variety of media and the diverse means through which it fosters poetry, the Woodberry Poetry Room has traditionally had a published poet as curator, thus assuring that the Harvard Library has at least one poet in residence.

The Woodberry Poetry Room just before it was moved to Lamont.

1936

Littauer Library and
Kennedy School Library

In April 1936, a few months after the Littauer Foundation gift established the Graduate School of Public Administration, the Committee on Public Documents stated that the library of the new school could not be built from the ground up but rather on the foundation of collections existing elsewhere in the Library. This came to mean that the Littauer Library functions as a collection serving the special needs of the Economics and Government departments, with holdings that are largely complementary to those elsewhere at Harvard. Littauer also has some special collections, including a large assemblage of labor material now known as the Slichter Industrial Relations Collection.

In 1978 the Kennedy School of Government Library was established. More than ever, it was impractical to build from the ground up research collections that already existed elsewhere, and the goal set for the new library was that it support instruction. Its model was the Woodrow Wilson Public Affairs Library at Princeton. With respect to the scope of the collection, the model was workable at Harvard, but not with respect to cataloging. At Princeton, a much more centralized university, books are processed by the central library, but Harvard's decentralization precludes such an arrangement, except by special treaty. There was no special treaty, and books at the Kennedy School were often placed uncataloged on the shelves under the name of the author. It, of course, soon became necessary to create a library encompassing the usual functions, and the library that started without a cataloging staff is now the only faculty library to have all of its holdings recorded in machine-readable form. Its 31,000 books emphasize the public-policy aspects of subjects of interest to a school that trains managers in the public sector. Many of them, especially books on the media and large parts of the collection of working papers, are not held elsewhere in the University.

The Littauer Center of Public Administration which houses the Library of the Kennedy School of Government.

The Littauer Library is located in this building.

1937

Keyes D. Metcalf

Keyes D. Metcalf (1899–1983), Librarian of Harvard College and Director of the Harvard University Library from 1937 to 1955, was the first library school graduate to guide the Library system. He may be generally remembered for new buildings — Houghton, New England Deposit Library, Lamont — but he also brought about a revolution in Library personnel. For the first time graduates of library schools and those with experience elsewhere were systematically recruited. To effect this change, pay scales and status necessarily had to improve. Harvard librarians of the pre-Metcalf era had traditionally been young people with no training who learned to do things the Harvard way and then continued to do so throughout their careers. The Metcalf recruits were much more mobile; many later accepted positions elsewhere. The staff of the Harvard Library became a part of the national community of librarians.

Just as many of those who moved on demonstrated by their subsequent careers as leaders of the profession that Metcalf was building a strong staff, so did those who stayed. Metcalf particularly valued talents that supplemented his own, and one of his achievements was to bring William A. Jackson to Harvard.

Metcalf also expanded the role of the library staff. He advocated, as early as 1945, that responsibility for book selection be placed in the hands of librarian specialists, the first of whom was appointed in 1953-54. There are now seven book selectors in the Book Selection Division in Widener, each of whom covers materials in the Roman alphabet in a linguistic and/or geographic area, a departure from the division by subject common in other universities. Selection of materials in non-Roman alphabets is also carried out by librarians in specialized departments. In most other parts of the University

Keyes D. Metcalf.

Library as well, book selection is the responsibility of librarian selectors, though faculty continue to advise.

Of course, Harvard librarians had done some book selection earlier. From the beginning of the nineteenth century, one finds librarians making suggestions for purchases. Sibley's choice of gifts to solicit was certainly a form of selection. In the 1930s librarians were also selecting materials in certain fields, and those who did the actual ordering selected books as well. Metcalf's innovation further professionalized librarianship and insured that specialists of high caliber would work with the faculty to put the right books on Harvard's shelves.

Paul H. Buck (1955–1964), who had formerly been Provost of the University, continued Metcalf's revolution in personnel by correcting inequities among librarians, further improving salaries, and narrowing the gap between librarians and faculty in other respects.

1938

Widener Automates
Its Circulation Records

Just as the history of automation in general goes back to the punched cards that aided French silk weavers in the early eighteenth century, so does library automation begin with punched cards. One of their first uses was in an adaptation of McBee Keysort punched cards for the purpose of maintaining circulation records. This was carried out in 1938 in Widener Library by Frederick G. Kilgour, who had the title of General Assistant. His work then was prophetic, for Kilgour went on to develop the Online Computer Library Center (OCLC), a national database of computerized cataloging records.

The basic library loan record is the file arranged by call numbers. However, it is also necessary to determine when books are overdue. In order to have access to both types of information, Widener Library used to maintain two different files. Punched cards made it possible to have only one.

Cards were notched to indicate the due date, so that by running a sorting needle through a particular hole it was possible to retrieve the books due on a specific date. Use of the cards along with other changes resulting from Kilgour's analysis of the circulation records reduced annual expenses by $3,500. The system was widely adopted elsewhere in the 1940s and 1950s.

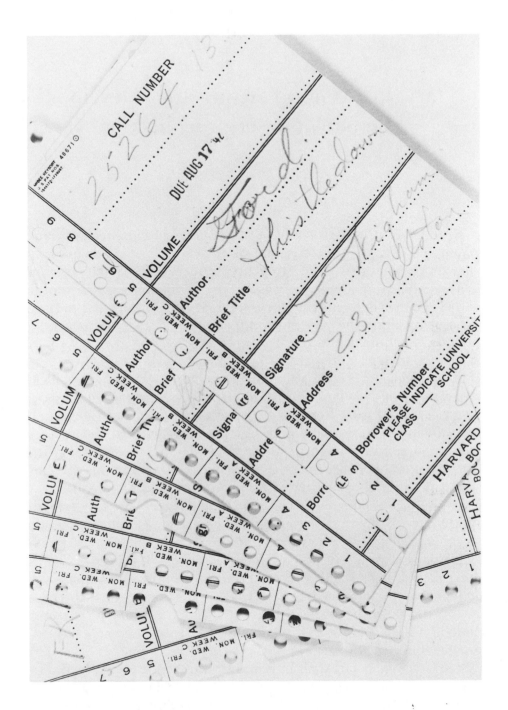

Circulation cards from 1942 with notches for sorting by means of a needle.

Harvard's "Grand Acquisitor" Develops
a Great Manuscript Collection

A publisher is now bringing out the *Catalogue of Manuscripts in the Houghton Library*. It records one of the world's great manuscript collections, one that, like so many other parts of the Harvard Library's holdings, owes its greatness not so much to age as to other factors. In the eighteenth century, the Harvard Library did not seek codices, let alone the papers of individuals. Neither did it acquire them in the nineteenth century, or even the first decades of the twentieth, with exceptions.

The individual who primarily brought about the change was William A. Jackson (1905–1964), who came to Harvard as Assistant Librarian in charge of the Treasure Room in 1938 and became the first Librarian of the Houghton Library in 1942. He knew that Harvard had no long tradition of acquiring the papers of individuals. Indeed, collecting such materials was not in vogue in other universities either, but this specialist in early English books perceived that he had a collecting opportunity, which, if lost, would never again occur. While also immensely strengthening Harvard's holdings of rare printed books, he set out to gather the papers of leading authors, especially of New England: Alcott, Aldrich, Dickinson, Emerson, Higginson, Holmes, Howells, Longfellow, Lowell, Melville, and others. Aided by his personal qualities — extraordinary intelligence, enormous capacity for work, and great personal charm — and by the threat of war and the war itself, plus the enticement of Houghton's splendid storage conditions, Jackson became Harvard's "grand acquisitor."

Like Coolidge's, Jackson's importance transcended what he did for Harvard. Coolidge played a major role in internationalizing the collections of American libraries and thereby enabling the United States to function in the international community as an informed partner. Jackson stimulated American libraries to collect personal papers, the use of which will long continue to enrich American culture.

William A. Jackson in 1950.

1938

Philip Hofer Joins the
Harvard Library Staff

Among the individuals who with passionate dedication have assembled the materials of scholarship for the Harvard Library, Philip Hofer (1898–1984), class of 1921, stands out as the "prince of the eye." With the discernment of the born collector, he devoted nearly half a century and a great deal of his personal fortune to enlarging the Library's store of well printed

and illustrated books, preferably ones with texts that were also significant. He worked as well to emphasize the cultural significance of the means of recording and spreading knowledge through the art and production of the book. Hofer's gifts to the Department of Printing and Graphic Arts that he founded, the first such department in a university library, may well be the most valuable ever made to the Library.

Such measurements are not easily made, because Hofer collected books so different from those gathered by Coolidge, to whom the Library owes so many of the great collections of historical sources. The same quality in literature and fine printing was attained more recently through the work of Jackson and Hofer and their successors.

If Harvard had been alone in emphasizing literature and the graphic arts, it would be reasonable to assume that the existence of strong historical collections had led to a shift in emphasis in order to fill a gap. But the same emphasis can be seen in the collecting of other libraries as well. The development of descriptive and analytical bibliography helped foster it, for bibliography gave early editions greater scholarly importance. Yet it is also as if the experience of the twentieth century, which has deprived history of its utility as a guide to future developments or as a source of noble and moral exemplars, has reduced the impetus for forming historical collections. In the face of the madness of our century, we seem instead to seek reassurance about the nobility of the human spirit and to turn for it to the finest works of the human mind in literature and the arts.

The shift in collecting, however it may be explained, has made the Harvard Library notable for the quality of the books on its shelves, and the purposes that they may serve include the intangible. As Jackson put it, "At any moment, the sight of any one of them may be the spark which will kindle in some young scholar the desire to unravel the complex which makes them important for mankind and set forth on a scholarly adventure which may result in one more solid addition to the structure of man's understanding of his past."

Philip Hofer in 1965.

The Houghton Library Opens

Thanks to a gift from Arthur A. Houghton, Jr., the College Library's rare books could be moved in 1942 into an almost perfect environment in the first rare book library constructed at an American university. It has been described as "the most advanced library building in the United States, if not in the world" at the time it opened, and its "basic principles . . . are still standard for the design of rare-book libraries." The housing offered by the Houghton Library was not just an incremental improvement; it was the first adequate storage for Harvard's rare books.

Since Gore Hall was an inadequate building, rare books stored there were necessarily in an inadequate environment. They did, however, from Gore's opening in 1841, have some security. The rarest of the Americana were placed in cupboards in the Reading Room. President Sparks's American historical manuscripts, which came to the Library after his death, were kept in his black walnut locked presses. Justin Winsor provided secure storage for rare books in the stack wing erected in 1877 by placing locked closets with heavy wire fronts in the aisles at the end of sections of shelves. The new wing constructed in 1902 had a mezzanine room to hold rare books. George Parker Winship, who became Assistant Librarian in charge of the Treasure Room in Widener in 1915, has described the shelving devised by Librarian William Coolidge Lane for that mezzanine room:

This was an arrangement for shelving the books in contiguous sliding wooden closets that locked automatically but could be pulled out as required, each containing a double row of shelves opening on the opposite sides. Ideal in theory as planned, the mechanical gadgets sometimes balked, wood swelled, and the books had no ventilation. I was then in Providence, where I tried twice to have this scheme developed in metal, but found no way of matching the joinery of wood at any cost within reason. I still believe that it ought to be possible, and that Harvard, and Mr. Lane, will sometime be credited, not for the first time, with being in the forefront in a matter of library practice.

Winship is, of course, describing what we term compact shelving, the space-saving method of storage that almost eighty years later began to come into widespread use in Harvard's libraries.

When space for rare books was planned in the Widener Library, it proceeded, according to Winship, on the assumption that the Harry Elkins Widener collection gave Harvard some monetarily valuable books for the first time and that few others needed special protection. The result was insufficient space for rare books in the Treasure Room on the first floor of Widener (the area now occupied by the Cataloging and Processing Department). The shortage was exacerbated by a welcome flood of gifts elicited by better storage conditions than Gore had provided. In addition, Winship, as Harvard's first rare book specialist, culled valuable books from the stacks. A stack area had to be built in the basement, where the books were threatened by possible flooding from ground water or burst pipes and were steadily damaged by the warmth from the heating pipes.

Since the opening of the Houghton Library, Harvard's other rare book collections have one by one found housing that is secure and environmentally adequate. It is also now generally recognized that all Harvard's books, not just those considered rare, need to be safeguarded from fluctuations of temperature and humidity and from pollutants in the air.

Above: The Treasure Room in Gore Hall in 1912.
The compact shelving can be seen at the back in the center;
below: The Treasure Room in Widener in 1915.

The Houghton stacks in 1942.

The William King Richardson Room on the second floor of Houghton in 1951.

1943

Radcliffe Starts to Form a Research Library on the History of Women

Since the 1977 agreement between Radcliffe and Harvard, women students receive Harvard diplomas, but Radcliffe continues to influence the lives of women at Harvard in a number of ways, one of the most significant being the collections and activities of the Schlesinger Library. Begun as the Women's Archives in 1943, it then housed only Maud Wood Park's collection on the woman's suffrage movement. Wilbur K. Jordan, president of Radcliffe College, and Professor Arthur Meier Schlesinger, Sr. (who in 1922 had termed "unthinkable" the neglect of "woman as a positive influence in American history") saw this first collection as the nucleus of a research library. Other collections were added. When the impact of the women's movement reached the academic world in the mid-1970s, Radcliffe had the scholarly resources. Whereas the Library served only a few scholars in 1949 and 247 users in 1969-70, the number of researchers who consult its holdings each year now exceeds 5,000.

The Arthur and Elizabeth Schlesinger Library on the History of Women in America, as the Women's Archives was renamed in 1965, is unusual for actually creating sources and furthering study in its field beyond Radcliffe and Harvard. Its Black Women Oral History Project documented the lives of black women through interviews and photographs; copies of interview transcripts have been deposited in other institutions, and the resulting exhibition went on national tour. The Schlesinger Library also administered a grant to help local libraries address concerns of women, and in another program, teachers and administrators in local public schools are using the Library to develop new curriculum materials that demonstrate the wide variety of roles and responsibilities assumed by women.

The Schlesinger Library's concept of the role of a library seems to have influenced others. Lectures, seminars, conferences, meetings, and concerts all probably exist in greater profusion throughout the Harvard Library than they would without its example.

The poster from an exhibition prepared by the Schlesinger Library.

Rush Hour at Widener Circulation Desk Stimulates Construction of Lamont

Space for books and people (both staff and readers) was the most pressing issue facing Keyes D. Metcalf, when he became Librarian of Harvard College and Director of the Harvard University Library in 1937. Widener, then only twenty-two years old, was full. In his Annual Report for 1939-40 Metcalf outlined a policy of decentralization: a building to house rare books and manuscripts, a storage library for infrequently used materials, a separate undergraduate library, and an underground library beneath the southeast corner of the Yard. All were eventually built: Houghton and New England Deposit Library in 1942, Lamont in 1949, and Pusey in 1976.

Additional decentralization also took place. Music books were transferred from Widener to the Eda Kuhn Loeb Music Library when it opened in 1956, and fine arts books in Widener were joined to those in the Fogg Art Museum to form the Fine Arts Library in 1962-63. Major amounts of materials relating to education were added to the holdings of the Gutman Library of the School of Education; among other transfers, many science materials have been moved to the Cabot Science Library, and cookbooks to the Schlesinger Library.

This policy has for forty years kept space from being a crucial determinant of the collecting and services of the College Library. It has also made Harvard a community in which books are everywhere, inescapably so.

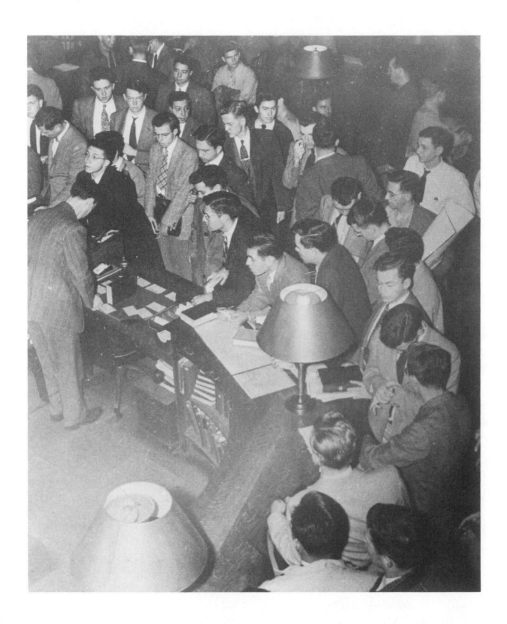

The opening of Lamont Library put a stop to scenes like this.

1954

Middle Eastern Collection

Archibald Cary Coolidge developed great Western-language collections about the Middle East, and in the half century since his death the Harvard Library has built major holdings in the languages of the area. This is the most recent expansion of the geographical and linguistic scope of the Library.

The Middle Eastern Collection, which consisted of about twenty Arabic books in 1830, began to grow substantially after James R. Jewett was appointed the first professor of Arabic in 1911. Until that time Arabic materials were acquired as an adjunct to Hebraic studies; afterwards they were collected for the study of Arabic literature itself. By 1949 there were about 2,500 Arabic books.

Great growth in the collection of books in the Middle Eastern languages began in 1954 with the advent of the Center for Middle Eastern Studies. In 1959, the Middle Eastern bibliographer Labib Zuwiyya Yamak was appointed to build a research collection, and the Middle Eastern Division was organized in 1962. Its cataloged monographs alone now number more than 100,000. In addition to strong Arabic holdings, the Library has the best Armenian collection in the country, and extensive collections of Persian, Turkish, and Urdu. Pashtu, Baluchi, Brahui, Kurdish, Turkoman, and Sindhi are other languages covered by significant holdings.

The Middle Eastern Department gathers such materials, first of all, for Harvard students, teachers, and researchers, but it also seeks to build a national resource to help Americans better understand the Middle East. More than that, though, it acts out of a belief that Arab civilization is a significant chapter of the human experience and that preserving its written heritage is valuable in itself. That is the motive that necessarily lies behind great collections, and the Harvard Middle Eastern Collection is now among the finest.

HEBREW GRAMMAR

WITH

A COPIOUS

Syntax and Praxis.

BY MOSES STUART

PROF. OF SACRED LITERATURE IN THEOL. SEM. AT ANDOVER.

1821.

ANDOVER:

FLAGG AND GOULD....PRINTERS.

(c) אִם *ne;* Hos. xii. 12. Job. xxxix. 13. xvii. 13, 16. xix. 5. But אִם usually implies a negative question, not a simple negation.

4. הֲלֹא (compounded of הֲ and לֹא,) *nonne?* but also equivalent in many cases to הִנֵּה, *ἰδού, ecce;* as the corresponding Arabic Particles are; Deut. xi. 30. Job. iv. 21. viii. 10. Prov. viii. 1. xiv. 22. xxii. 20. 2 Kings xx. 20, compare 2 Chron. xxxii. 32. 2 Kings xxi. 17, comp. 2 Chron. xxxiii. 18. 2 Kings xxii. 23, comp. 2. Chron. xxxv. 27. In all the cases of comparison, where the writer in Kings uses הֲלֹא, the writer in Chron uses הִנָּם *ecce illa! ecce!* In the same manner, the Arabians use أَلَا أَلَّا هَلَا هَلَّا, &c, for *ἰδού, ecce!*

§ 237.

Of Prepositions.

1. Composite Prepositions, *in some cases*, do not differ in sense from the simple forms.

Thus מֵאַחֲרֵי=אַחֲרֵי i. e. *after;* מֵעַל=עַל *on, upon;* מִן=לְמִן *from, of.*

The first printing of Arabic in an American book.

179

1960

Countway Library of Medicine

In 1800 Ward Nicholas Boylston presented about 1,100 medical volumes to Harvard. Considering the gift and the tendency of physicians to be bibliophiles, it would be natural to assume that the Medical School soon developed one of the finest Harvard libraries. That did not happen. Until 1871 its professors, instead of being paid salaries, received students' lecture fees, not a system to encourage building a school's library.

The library situation did not soon improve under Harvard auspices. Archibald Cary Coolidge wrote to his counterpart at Columbia on 25 February 1913: "As for the Medical School — The library question there is in . . . a mess. . . . There has been no central Harvard Medical Library. At one time there were fifteen separate ones. These have now got down to five and there is a strong movement . . . for combining these five into one. . . . Until now the Harvard Medical School has not tried to keep books that were not immediately useful and has turned over all the older ones to the Library of the Boston Medical Association."

A great medical library did, however, begin at the time when the Medical School was revitalized in the 1870s; in 1875 the Boston Medical Library was resuscitated, and it developed by 1960 into the third largest medical library in the United States. That year agreement was reached to merge the Boston Medical Library and the Library of the Harvard Medical School in a new building, the Francis A. Countway Library of Medicine. The building was made possible by a gift from Sandra Countway. The union resulted in the second largest medical library in the country.

In some areas, such as medical incunabula, the collection is unrivaled, and it has since become one of the great repositories of papers

of individuals and archives of institutions, many of which are useful
to social historians as well as historians of medicine.

The Francis A. Countway Library of Medicine.

1962

Judaica Collection

Cotton Mather (class of 1678) described Harvard as being in the heart of the *Kirjath-Sepher* (a Hebrew expression meaning City of Books). The statement is more true today. No city of comparable size in the world has so many books. Among those books is the nation's largest university collection of Judaica.

John Harvard's bequest included several items of Judaica. Other Hebrew books continued to arrive as gifts, for Harvard men graduated with some knowledge of the language. Until 1755 Hebrew was a required course. Instruction in the language continued, but its purpose was to enable students to read the Scripture in the original.

With the establishment of the Littauer Professorship of Hebrew Literature and Philosophy in 1925, it became necessary to form a broad collection for research on all aspects of the history, thought, and literature of the Jewish people in all ages. The private library of Ephraim Deinard was acquired in 1929. Felix Friedmann's came in 1951, and Lee M. Friedman's gift of his collection in 1957 elevated the Harvard Library to a position of eminence in the field.

Shortly thereafter, in 1962, the endowment of the post of Lee M. Friedman Bibliographer in Judaica and the establishment of the Judaica Department enabled the Library to develop the collection intensively. To help in the effort, friends of the Library have established nearly 300 endowed Judaica book funds.

In addition to developing a comprehensive collection for scholars at Harvard, the Department is doing much to make the collection a resource for the world of scholarship. A major part of the collection has been preserved in microform, and the Department is automating the Hebrew and Yiddish catalogs in order to disseminate both texts and bibliographical data around the world. The Harvard Library is making it possible for other cities to be a *Kirjath-Sepher*.

חמשה חומשי
תורה
ונביאים ראשונים ואחרונים
וכתובים
נדפסו
באמשטירדם
בבית מנשה בן ישראל
והוגהו בחשק האהבת עלידו
שנת ישע יה

במצות איש היחם והמעלה
שמו הינדריק לורינציאום

This Hebrew Bible published in Amsterdam in 1635, was owned by Judge
Samuel Sewall (1671), two undergraduates, President Benjamin Wadsworth, and
his nephew of the same name.

183

1963

The Library Takes
Major Steps in Automation

Just as the U.S. federal system of government makes possible experimentation by states, the decentralization at Harvard enables individual libraries to explore new paths. The first to use computer technology at Harvard was the Library of the Schools of Medicine and Public Health in 1961, followed by the Business School Library. Next was the College Library, which installed a punched card circulation system in July 1963. It was seen as a stage in an evolutionary approach to automation, the total system concept having then been rejected because of the size and complexity of the Library.

Among further possibilities considered was conversion of the shelflist, the list of books in the order in which they stand on the shelves. Begun in the nineteenth century, the shelflist was on large folio sheets which were gathered into sheaves. As entries were added, manual recopying often became necessary. Although computerization would make for more legible records and save the expense of recopying, its cost could not be justified if the shelflist were to serve only the traditional functions. Then, it was realized that if one were to convert, for instance, the Ital class, the section of the Library containing Italian history and literature, the computer could sort the entries to produce an alphabetical and chronological list of holdings on Italian history and literature, as well as a list in shelflist order. If these lists were published, the project would then serve additional purposes both at Harvard and elsewhere. Following a successful pilot project completed by January 1965, sixty volumes were published in the Widener Shelflist Series by March 1977.

The Widener shelflist project, along with a number of immediate benefits, prepared the way for the future, both through adding equipment and developing a trained staff. Moreover, data processing became part of the organizational structure, with its own budget.

184

A page from the Widener shelflist.

1966

Lamont Opens Its Doors to Women

In the year 1966 a cause of anger about the Harvard Library was removed. Radcliffe students were permitted to use Lamont, and for the first time all the Harvard libraries were open to women.

The earliest noted expression of anger about exclusion from the Harvard Library appears in Mary A. Livermore's *The Story of My Life* (Hartford, Conn., 1897). It recounts an episode that probably occurred about the mid-1830s. "One of my cousins, who was studying at Harvard College, had taken two or three of my girl companions and myself, through the College Library, whose magnitude filled us with wonder. He impressed the fact upon us at every step that it was not open to women and girls. I was so hurt at what I felt to be an unjust prohibition, that I secretly resolved never again to cross the threshold of that Library. . . ." Mary A. Livermore was born in 1820, and the cousin was very likely Abiel Abbot Livermore, who after graduation in 1833 stayed on as a graduate student for three years.

Later students of the Society for the Collegiate Instruction of Women (the so-called Harvard Annex), incorporated in 1882, were, upon special written application, permitted to use the Gore Hall Library. The application needed the signature of a sponsor, and Thomas Wentworth Higginson and William James, among others, were willing to sign. Those few women apparently had equal access with men to the library until late in 1888 or very early in 1889 when Librarian Justin Winsor established a reading room for women. Arthur Gilman, the Cambridge resident who had been involved in the founding of the Annex, wrote to Winsor on 5 January 1889 that a special reading room would actually reduce access for some women.

Keep the Girls in Lamont

They've been letting Cliffies into Lamont for close to two weeks now and lo! the hallowed walls have not fallen. In fact, the short tenure of emergency coeducation in Lamont has accomplished what years of verbiage could not — proven, once and for all, that people can study for Harvard degrees in a heterosexual library.

There now seems to be no reason for the library administrators to fulfill their promise and end the arrangement on Sunday. In fact, there is more reason than ever to allow Cliffies to use Lamont.

The new Hilles Library in the Radcliffe Quad is attractive, comfortable, and convenient for Cliffies to use for taking out reserve books at night. But during the day, when the girls are in the Square and might like to spend a spare hour between classes looking at a reserve book, there is no place for them to go. While Radcliffe once housed its books midway between the Quad and the Square (and conveniently across the street from the Graduate Center where many Cliffies eat lunch), now there is nothing but an intellectual wasteland stretching the long mile up Garden Street.

Furthermore, Hilles's location should relieve Harvard men of what seems to have been their chief grounds for barring Cliffies: the fear that the girls, like locusts, will descend at 9 p.m. to pick reserve book shelves clean. It would be a rare Cliffie who would choose to trudge to Lamont just to get a book when a much more attractive building sat just a few steps outside her door. Nor would Cliffies be likely to brave the snows of January reading period to crowd the boys out of their accustomed carrels.

Letting girls stay in Lamont would work no hardship on the boys (who are, after all, free to use Hilles if they should be passing by), and would be one less inconvenience for Cliffies. The administrators merely have to view what was an emergency measure as an experiment—one that has succeeded.

The *Harvard Crimson* of 6 October 1966
on the issue of opening Lamont to women.

187

Above: The Radcliffe Library, on the top floor of Fay House, in the 1890s;
below: The Hilles Library.

Of course, he was correct, and a plan of the Widener building published in the winter of 1949 shows that Winsor's decision also had the long-term consequence of a special Radcliffe Reading Room in Widener; it was the small room immediately to the left of the elevator on the second floor, a space now occupied by the Interlibrary Loan Division. Radcliffe women who were graduate students had access to the Widener stacks, but undergraduates could work only in that room. After Lamont opened in 1949, the reserve book operation was moved there from the main reading room. Not long thereafter Radcliffe women were permitted to use the main reading room.

Radcliffe had had a separate library building since 1908, half of its cost paid for by Andrew Carnegie, but it got a truly great library building in 1966. The Susan Morse and Frederick Whiley Hilles Library opened in September 1966, just at the time that women gained admission to Lamont. The architect, in seeking what he termed "an ambiance . . . that related in scale and in character to the feminine" actually produced "a sympathetic and human library environment." Women and men both have made it the most popular library in the Harvard/Radcliffe community.

1981

The Library Inaugurates
a Microfiche Catalog

In the nineteenth century the size of the collection and its growth made the traditional book catalog impractical for Harvard and stimulated the Library to carry out a major innovation — the card catalog. In the twentieth century, when computerized cataloging and an online catalog have become realistic possibilities, the size and decentralization of Harvard's collections have stimulated the Library to automate, but those same factors necessitate that it do so cautiously. The policy has been stage-by-stage, carefully planned development in which the greatest possible benefit has been sought at the lowest possible cost.

The first major step was the Distributable Union Catalog (DUC) on microfiche, instituted in 1981. Before the DUC, the only union catalog for most of Harvard's nearly 100 libraries was located in Widener, and it essentially consisted only of author entries. With the DUC, users at any of the 180 DUC microfiche readers can easily determine whether a recently published book is held anywhere at Harvard, and they can do so by title and subject as well as by author.

Ultimately, users will be able to search a computer-supported central database.

1981

Harvard Receives the First Major
Private Funds for Preservation

Preservation is not a new problem for libraries. About 1780 a Harvard graduate wrote to President Wigglesworth complaining of the "want of loose papers" with which to cover books when loaned. The records of the Library are full of expressions of concern about the need to bind and preserve what is already here, and various versions of the Library Laws, from the seventeenth century on, have provisions relating to the preservation of books.

By the 1980s it had become clear that the terms of the problem had changed. Earlier, the question was whether copies at Harvard would continue to be preserved and available. Now, it is whether the texts of millions of books of the nineteenth and twentieth centuries will continue to be preserved and available anywhere at all. About the middle of the nineteenth century, books began to be printed on paper that eventually rots because of the sizing and the chemicals used in its production. Such paper is still in use, and most packages of new books increase the number that will turn brittle. Nearly half of the books in Widener are now so fragile that even careful users break off corners, if not whole pages. And those same books are in the same deteriorated condition in libraries around the world. Large amounts of money are needed to upgrade the environmental conditions in which the books are housed, for this will prolong their life. An improved environment will provide time for the large-scale, coordinated copying onto microfilm or other media that is essential if we are to pass on the texts to succeeding generations.

The copying will require major funds. Support for filming several million pages has been received as Title II-C grants under the Strengthening Research Libraries Resources Program of the U.S. Department of Education. Private funds have also begun to be available. In 1981 the Lucius N. Littauer Foundation made a grant of

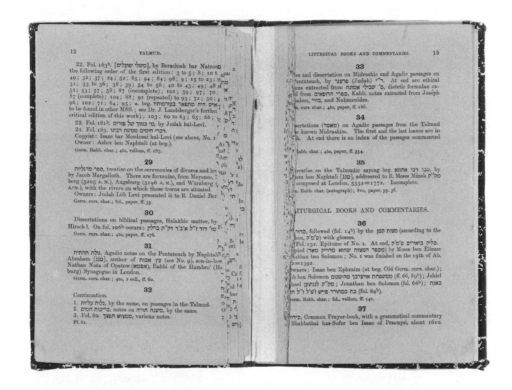

Because the pages of this book broke off when turned, it could not even be preserved on microfilm. It is neccessary to locate another copy, have it disbound, and then microfilmed.

Israeli election posters preserved in microform by the Judaica Department.

194

$500,000 for the filming of the Library's Judaica holdings, the largest preservation endowment yet established. A conference on preservation held in celebration of the gift brought together librarians from around the world, university administrators, foundation executives, and private individuals interested in the problem. The publicity generated by the gift and the conference helped bring more widespread attention to the need for preservation.

The same year the Tudor Foundation, Inc., increased the Aaron and Clara Greenhut Rabinowitz Fund for conservation in the University Library from $100,000 to $250,000.

As the thirty-fifth decade of the Library's history begins, preservation looms as its largest problem.

1985

HOLLIS Begins Operation

On 1 July 1985 the Harvard On-Line Library Information System began operation. Its acronym, HOLLIS, recalls the great eighteenth-century donors to the Harvard Library. Cataloging had been automated earlier. HOLLIS now offers libraries the capability to perform on-line the other steps necessary to put new books on the shelves — from placing orders on through keeping track of the stages of processing, paying invoices, and maintaining book fund accounts. In addition to making routine work more efficient, HOLLIS promises to help solve the problem of unnecessary duplication. For the first time a librarian in one library can easily determine whether a book is on order or in-process in another library, and decisions to buy duplicates can be rational, rather than by-products of decentralization.

HOLLIS is a major step toward an on-line catalog to replace the DUC. In the near future, scholars and students, seated at terminals and microcomputers in libraries, offices, dormitories and homes, will be able to search the HOLLIS catalog interactively. Harvard Library users will then have the advantage of distributability offered by the published catalog, plus even more points of access than the card catalog could offer, and more timely information than either it or the microfiche DUC could provide.

Just as the card catalog of 1862 required an enormous effort, so did HOLLIS. Its staff put in long hours, as did the many working groups who devised the functions, specifications, and policies for HOLLIS. The necessity that it fill the needs of many diverse libraries made HOLLIS the largest collective effort in the Library's history. There is a cost to that, one that centralized institutions do not need to bear, but the effort insured success and has helped Harvard to remain a university in which books are everywhere.

THE HARVARD LIBRARIAN

issued from the OFFICE OF THE DIRECTOR
HARVARD UNIVERSITY LIBRARY
Cambridge, Massachusetts 02138

ISSN 0073-0564
Vol. 17, No. 2 September 1983
Pamela Matz, *Editor*

Pew Trust Awards Grant for On-Line Acquisitions System

The Pew Memorial Trust has awarded a grant of $1.2 million to the Harvard University Library to support the purchase and development of an on-line acquisitions system.

In accepting the grant, Derek Bok, President of Harvard University, said, "Harvard is grateful to the Pew Memorial Trust for their generous and timely grant to the University Library, one of Harvard's and the nation's great educational resources. The support from the Pew Memorial Trust will enable the Library to expand and improve its services to members of the University community and to countless scholars and visitors from around the world."

"This magnanimous grant from the Pew Memorial Trust enables the Library to begin a complex and costly project which will result in more efficient service to library users," commented Oscar Handlin, Carl H. Pforzheimer University Professor and Director of the University Library. "Of even greater importance is the recognition by a major foundation, one which traditionally encourages innovation and excellence, of the value of the Harvard collections and their contribution to scholarship. I speak for all my colleagues in saying that the confidence expressed by the trustees of the Pew Memorial Trust in our efforts to use the computer to facilitate serious study of the arts and sciences is gratifying indeed."

One of the largest foundations in the United States, the Trust awards grants in the areas of education, health care, human services, and arts and humanities. Library needs are a funding priority, and the Pew Memorial Trust has made generous gifts to libraries throughout the country, with special attention to computerization of library services, renovation of facilities, and development of regional sharing of resources. Previous grants to Harvard University include major funding of programs of the Harvard School of Public Health, the Harvard Medical School, and Radcliffe College. *(continued on page 2)*

HOLLIS

Implementation of the new on-line acquisitions system is a complex process that must be studied and planned in detail, but one decision has been easily made: the new system has been named the Harvard On-Line Library Information System—HOLLIS. The choice of the name HOLLIS is a particularly felicitious one, as the Hollis family were early benefactors of Harvard. Thomas Hollis, of London, made generous gifts of books to the Harvard Library and a descendant also named Thomas Hollis left a legacy that, in 1774, established the Library's first book fund.

Preservation Microfilming Grant Renewed

Preservation microfilming by the University Library will be supported during the year beginning on 1 October 1983 by a grant of $249,834 under the Strengthening Research Libraries Resources Program of the U.S. Department of Education. The grant will pay the salaries of a small staff: the project coordinator; a half-time assistant to the coordinator; two half-time librarians, one a specialist in European publications and the other a Slavic specialist; and a half-time assistant working with Slavic materials. It will enable the Library to preserve, dissem-

inate, and facilitate the use of approximately 1.2 million pages of fragile and rare (in some cases, unique) publications and manuscripts. During 1983–84, the Library will give special attention to its outstanding collection of European publications of the World War II period and will continue its experimentation in preservation and bibliographical control of collections of ephemera. (These collections include holdings in the Baker, Andover-Harvard, Fine Arts, Widener, and Schlesinger libraries and the University Archives.) Funding has been received
(continued on page 3)

The Harvard Librarian announces a grant that was essential to the realization of
HOLLIS.

The World's Largest
Privately Supported Library

On 15 September 1714 President Leverett instructed the Treasurer to pay to John Rogers, "keeper of the library," his salary of £6. Most likely no books were purchased or bound, so except for a blank book to record borrowings from the Library, Rogers's salary may have been the sole expense.

Now the Harvard University Library has a professional staff of more than 300 FTEs (full-time equivalent employees) and support staff of about 520 FTEs. When student assistants are included, the total FTE staff numbers about 1,000.

Total expenditures for 1984-85 were $33,736,108. Such a figure, large as it is, scarcely bears comparison with the budgets of the great national libraries; they have much wider responsibilities and much greater resources to fulfill them. Yet in terms of collections, the Harvard Library, with 11.1 million volumes, is among the half dozen largest in the world, and the largest that is privately supported. In 1764 the Province of New Hampshire helped the Library rebuild; Massachusetts has given assistance; and recently the U.S. Department of Education has greatly furthered preservation. But the Harvard Library has essentially been built from the resources of the University, which stem to a large extent from private philanthropy. The generosity of individuals continues to be essential to the on-going work of the Library, perhaps above all in making innovation possible. Fortunately, the gifts of individuals are now being supplemented by donations from foundations. The Kresge Foundation, The Lucius N. Littauer Foundation, The Mellon Foundation, The Pew Foundation, and others are helping the Library go through another great period of modernization.

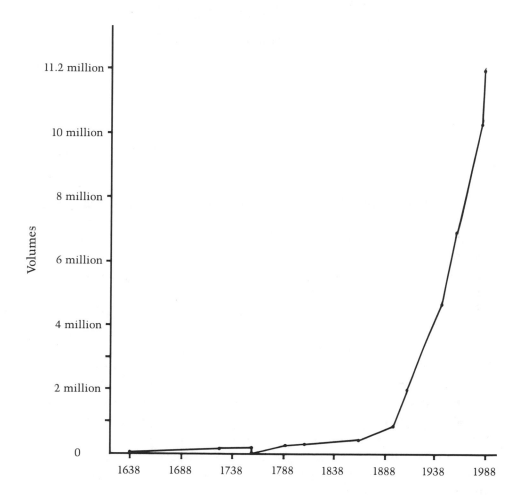

The growth of the Harvard Library.

1986

Harvard Builds a New
Storage Library

In the history of the Library, lack of space has inhibited change, and solutions to space problems have furthered other changes. Collecting is shaped by the amount of space, for its lack restrains buying, even accepting gifts. Harvard, at which a number of presidents have studied, does not, ironically, collect the papers of political figures. Surely, lack of space has been a major reason.

Services are shaped by space. In the Government Documents and Microforms Division the staff does its best with workspace insufficient for them or for users. Its location in an out-of-the-way, generally unattractive area, despite rapidly increasing use, also reflects space constraints. It is no accident that the Farnsworth Room for recreational reading, an experiment, was installed in Widener just after its opening. Lamont was built partly to alleviate space pressures in Widener. Although undergraduates had been agitating for a separate library for a century, they owe Lamont's existence to the fact that Widener was crowded and that Metcalf wisely used the need for more space to accomplish other goals as well.

When Metcalf had constructed the New England Deposit Library in 1942 to relieve space in Widener, he hoped it would also foster the goal of joint collection management among the region's libraries. Although this did not happen, his expectation was not unreasonable.

Now Harvard has built another storage library, known as the Harvard Depository. Located thirty-five minutes from Harvard Yard, it has a capacity to hold 1.7 million volumes or their equivalent. The Harvard Depository's innovative design permits very dense storage, and its single purpose has permitted the building to incorporate the most recent findings on preservation of materials. It is a major step toward housing safely all of the Library's collections. That space, the first major expansion in a decade, will surely effect other changes.

Two views of the Harvard Depository.
The bottom picture is taken from the forklift used to retrieve
and reshelve material.

1986

The Graduate School of Education Library
Adds a Research Collection

On 12 May 1986 the Gutman Library of the Graduate School of Education celebrated the gift of the archives of Action for Children's Television (ACT). In addition to print materials, the archives contains a large number of videotapes, and, though not the first to be accepted by a Harvard Library, this is the largest collection of the new medium to have been received. This may also be the first instance of the receipt of an archives that will be used daily by the creating organization. It is probable that researchers from a number of Harvard faculties will find the ACT archives a significant resource.

The Gutman Library of the Graduate School of Education is one of the faculty libraries that does not have total responsibility for the entire field or for the major portion of it. The School began as the Division of Education, with a library that "never aspired [as of 1954] to be more than a working collection for the students in the School." Gutman now has 150,000 volumes and is more than a working collection. Its holdings are particularly strong in the areas of the history, philosophy, theory, and practice of American primary and secondary education. The College Library, however, continues to be Harvard's major collection on education in parts of the world other than the United States. It also has the historical research collections, with the exception of the textbook collection, which has been transferred to Gutman Library. Important holdings relating to education also exist in other Harvard libraries, particularly the Andover-Harvard Theological Library and the Law School Library.

The Monroe C. Gutman Library of the Graduate School of Education.

1986

Records for Manuscripts and Archives
Are Made Available Nationally

The staff of the Manuscript and Archives Project have just created machine-readable bibliographical records for 5,000 collections in more than fifty repositories at Harvard and Radcliffe. Because the records are being entered into the RLIN database of cataloging records, scholars elsewhere will also be able to obtain information on one of the largest assemblages of manuscripts in the country.

This project, funded primarily by a grant from the National Historical Publications and Records Commission, was an effective response to one of the problems inherent in Harvard's decentralized library system — the difficulty of carrying out work that benefits the Harvard community and the wider world of scholarship more than it does the local library and its constituency. Harvard has long had a central catalog for books, but for other non-book materials, such as photographs, information on holdings is still inadequate. A first step was *Photographs at Harvard and Radcliffe: a Directory* (1984), but no one would claim that the need is satisfied.

The extent of the holdings is part of the problem, as is the fact that there are nearly 100 libraries. But the major difficulty in the way of a unified approach is the decentralization that mirrors the decentralization of the University itself. The various faculties of the University raise their own funds and spend them. A consequence is that the Director of the University Library does not direct, but rather coordinates — and without large, unallocated funds to persuade or to make possible work that benefits the whole but not necessarily the individual library and its regular users.

Decentralization earlier fostered the entrepreneurial building of collections. Whether decentralization will work as well in an era in which scholarship is increasingly interdisciplinary and libraries ever more interdependent is not clear.

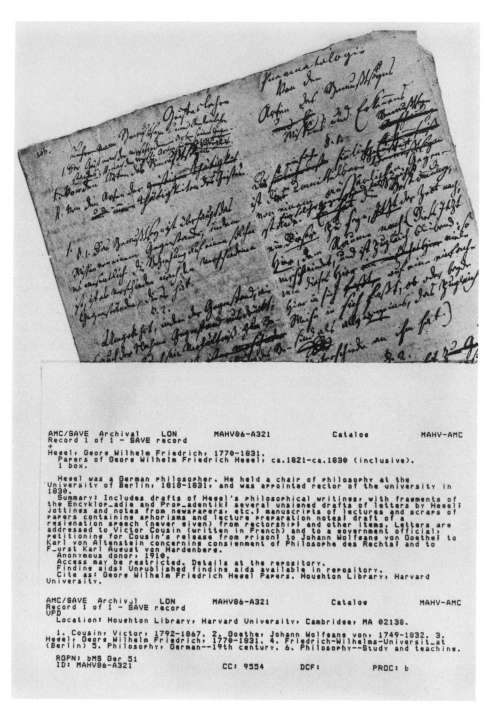

A Hegel manuscript and a printout describing the Hegel collection.

1986

The Widener Library Building Is Improved to Preserve Harvard's Books

The Widener building, along with containing sufficient space for the central collection, was a great forward step in housing the books safely. But buildings age, and the original copper roof, though it lasted sixty-five years, had to be retired in 1980. The new roof, made possible by a gift from the George D. Widener estate, is expected to be as durable.

Buildings also must change in response to new understanding of the dangers threatening books. Widener was, in fact, apparently designed to combat dampness, the major environmental problem of Gore Hall. And it provided so effectively for the circulation of air that to a later generation the stacks seemed to be a collection of chimneys. Keyes Metcalf took measures to reduce the possibility of a fire spreading to the stacks, and in 1967-68 ventilation slits were closed on every other stack level, stack stairways were enclosed, and smoke detectors were installed. Thus, another danger, was tackled.

We now know, which earlier generations did not, that all books need climate and humidity control to retard the decay of paper that is destroying the collections. In a major step toward that goal, made possible by the Roy E. Larsen bequest, the old windows were replaced. The next necessary step is updating the electrical system, which will further reduce the danger of fire as well as allow for the increased demands that modernization make.

Each generation the Harvard Library's staff and supporters have accomplished tasks that have enabled the Library to continue to carry out its mission effectively. This generation's major responsibility has become obvious. It is to preserve the books that Thomas Hollis gave to a College he never saw, the pamphlets that Sibley so assiduously begged, the unusual collections that Coolidge purchased en-bloc, the rare books and manuscripts that Jackson acquired, and the host of other books that many, many people added to the shelves.

A view of the roof over Widener Library.

207

List of Illustrations

Pages 38-39. Facing pages from an interleaved copy of the catalog of 1790. University Archives: UA III.50.15.39VT, copy B.

Page 41. Overseers Visiting Committee Report, dated 9 July 1799. University Archives: UA III.50.10.4VT.

Page 43. Shapleigh bookplate, in Library book-plates, 1764–1866. University Archives: UA III.50.15.20.

Page 45. Endorsed title: List of books added to the Library during the year ending August 1807. In box, Additions to the Library 1778–1858. University Archives: UA III.50.15.70.2.

Page 46. The record of the reading of freshman Eben R. Dorr in 1814-15. University Archives: UA III.50.15.60 (charging record for 1814-15).

Page 47. Page 11 of *Catalogue of Books, Which May Be Taken from the Library of Harvard University by Members of the Freshman Class* (Cambridge, Printed for the University, 1814). University Archives: HUF 523.14.

Page 49. This copy of Kirkland's appeal was sent to "Miss [Catherine Maria] Sedgwick" in Stockbridge. University Archives: UA III.50.15.139.

Page 51. Dane Hall. Law School Art Collection.

Page 52, *above*. Austin Hall Reading Room in 1902. Law School Art Collection.

Page 52, *below*. Langdell Hall Reading Room. Law School Art Collection.

Page 55. Israel Thorndike letter to John T. Kirkland, 17 June 1818. University Archives: UA III.50.28.18.

Page 57. George Ticknor in 1828. From [Hilliard, George S.] *Life, Letters, and Journals, of George Ticknor* (Boston and New York, Houghton Mifflin Co., 1909), vol. 1.

Pages 58-59. Accessions book for 1834–1841. University Archives: UA III.50.15.70.6.

Page 61. Andrews Norton. University Archives: HUP.

Page 61. Joseph G. Cogswell. Librarian's office, Widener Library.

Page 61. Charles Folsom. University Archives: HUP.

Page 61. Thaddeus William Harris. University Archives: HUP.

Page 63. Map Collection, Pusey Library. The note on p. 62 is on the verso of the map.

Page 65. Thomas Nuttall. University Archives: HUP.

Page 66. Catalogus Bibliothecae Institutionis Historiae Naturalis Massachusettensis, sub manu et curâ professoris. University Archives: UA III.50.28.26.

Page 69. *Regulations concerning the Use of the Public Library of Harvard University*, 1839. University Archives: HUF 523.6.73.

Page 71. A page from William Croswell's classified catalog. University Archives: UA III.50.15.42.2.

Page 72. Sample tray of cards from the Harris catalog (Cicero - Cla), plus one card. University Archives: UA III.50.15.44.8PF.

Page 75. Gore Hall. University Archives: HUV 48.

Page 76. Gore Hall with the addition of 1877. University Archives: HUV 48.

Page 77. Gore Hall's self-supporting stacks laid bare by the demolition crew. University Archives: HUV 48.

Page 78. Interior of Gore Hall before it was subdivided. University Archives: HUV 48.

Page 79, *above*. Gore Hall Reading Room about 1902.

Page 79, *below*. Delivery Room in 1912. Photos: Pach Brothers. University Archives: HUV 48pf.

Page 81. Subscription book recording donors to the Donation Fund of 1842. University Archives: UA III.28.41.2.

Page 83. Institute of 1770 charging record for 1849-52. University Archives: HUD 3461.750.5.

Page 85, *above*. Harvard College Treasurer's Journal, 1777–1785, on the desk of Treasurer Ebenezer Storer. University Archives: UA I.50.15.56VT. Photo: William Mercer.

Page 85, *below*. University Archives: Women Producing Records in Lehman Hall, 1949-50. News Office Photo, no. 2534.

Page 86. John Langdon Sibley in 1857. University Archives: HUP.

Page 87. Sibley's circular of 1856. University Archives: HUF 523.6.73.

Page 88. An issue of *Godey's Lady's Book, and Ladies' American Magazine* presented to the Harvard Library on 15 September 1842, by Sarah Josepha Hale. Houghton Library: P 201.1*.

Page 91. Vapereau, Gustave. *Dictionnaire universel des contemporains* (Paris, 1858). Widener Library: H 1058.58.

Page 93. Title page and flyleaf of Andrew Law's *The Rudiments of Music* ([Cheshire, Conn.], 1783). Houghton Library: Mus 492.69.2*.

Page 94, *above*. Students using photographs in the Visual Collections. Fine Arts Library.

Page 94, *below*. View across the photograph cabinets of the Visual Resources Collection in the Fine Arts Library Visual Resources Collection. Photo: Carol Dirga.

Page 96. A sketch of blocks for catalog drawers, from "Mr. Abbot's Statement Respecting the New Catalogues of the College Library," p. 42, in *Report of the Committee of the Overseers of Harvard College Appointed to Visit the Library for the Year 1863* (Boston, 1864). University Archives: UA III.50.5.

Page 97. A card from Abbot's subject catalog, reproduced actual size. University Archives: UA III.50.15.46.

Page 99. Bookplates in current use for various funds established in the 1870s and 1880s. Widener Library.

Page 101. The Tozzer Library.

Page 103. Justin Winsor's office. University Archives: HUP.

Page 104. Justin Winsor. University Archives: HUP.

Page 107. *Bibliographical Contributions*, no. 26.

Page 108. The Cabot Science Library in the Science Center. Photo: Susan L. Finnerty.

Page 109. Searching a scientific database in the Cabot Science Library. Photo: Susan L. Finnerty.

Page 110. A view of the Museum of Comparative Zoology Library. Photo: William Mercer.

Page 113. Justin Winsor's plan for centralizing the processing work of the various libraries. University Archives: UA III.50.15.140.2.

Page 114. Ivan Panin. From Class of 1882 album. University Archives: HUD 282.04pf.

Page 115. From *The Kilgour Collection of Russian Belles-Lettres.* (Cambridge, Mass., 1959).

Page 117. The Frances Loeb Library of the School of Design.

Page 119. Caricatures of Francis James Child, drawn by colleague William James. Reproduced from *Harvard Library Bulletin*, V (1951), opp. p. 314.

Page 120. James Russell Lowell, another major supporter of the Library, at Elmwood about 1865. Reproduced from *Harvard Library Bulletin*, V (1951), after p. 138.

Page 125. Garrick as Macbeth. Drawing by Jean Louis Fesch, ca. 1769. Harvard Theatre Collection.

Page 127. The Andover-Harvard Theological Library. Manuscripts Collection, Andover-Harvard Theological Library.

Page 129. The dedication of the Business School campus in June 1927. Manuscripts and Archives, Baker Library.

Page 131. Archibald Cary Coolidge in his office in Gore Hall. University Archives: HUP.

Page 132. Camões, Luiz de, *Os Lvsiadas* (Lisboa, 1572), the gift of John B. Stetson, Jr., 1926. Houghton Library: Port 5215.724*.

Page 133. Franck, Sebastian, *Weltbuch: spiegel und bildtnisz des gantzen erdtbodens von Sebastiano Franco* ([Tübingen] 1534), the gift of Archibald Cary Coolidge. Houghton: Geog 3205.34F*.

Page 135. Clipping from *Boston American*, 21 May 191(1?). University Archives: HUF 523.400.

Page 137. The Harry Elkins Widener Memorial Library.

Page 138. Randall Hall. University Archives: HUV 48.

Page 139. Temporary book stacks in Randall Hall. University Archives: HUV 48pf.

Page 140. Excavating for Widener Library. University Archives: HUV 49.

Page 141. Part of the stacks of Widener under construction. University Archives: HUV 49pf.

Page 144. The Widener Reading Room in the Library's early years. University Archives: HUV 49.

Page 145. Clipping from *Boston Herald*. University Archives: HUF 523.400

Page 147. The Farnsworth Room as depicted on a postcard, 1916. University Archives: HUV 49.

Page 149. The first publication of the John Barnard Associates. University Archives: HUD 3466.3000.

Page 151. A. Kaiming Chiu. Harvard-Yenching Library.

Page 153. The turnstile in Widener, 1930. University Archives: HUV 49.

Page 155. Woodberry Poetry Room just before it was moved to Lamont Library. University Archives: News Office Photo U 2210.

Page 157. The Littauer Center of Public Administration which houses the Library of the Kennedy School of Government. Photo: Michael Nagy.

Page 158. The building housing the Littauer Library.

Page 160. Keyes D. Metcalf. Photo: Karsh. University Archives: HUP.

Page 163. Circulation cards from 1942. University Archives: UA III.50.15.60. Photo: William W. Mercer.

Page 165. William A. Jackson in 1950. University Archives: HUP.

Page 168. Philip Hofer in 1965. University Archives: UAV.605.280.1p.

Page 171, *above*. The Treasure Room in Gore Hall in 1912. Photo: Pach Brothers. University Archives: HUV 48pf.

Page 171, *below*. The Treasure Room in Widener as depicted on a postcard, 1915. HUV 49.

Page 172. The Houghton stacks in 1942. University Archives: HUV 49B.

Page 173. The Richardson Room in 1951. University Archives: HUV 49B.

Page 175. Poster from a Schlesinger Library exhibition. Photograph by Benjamin Crown, Brattleboro, Vermont, 1918.

Page 177. The Circulation Desk in Widener before construction of Lamont Library, 1946. University Archives: HUV 49.

Page 179. Moses Stuart, *Hebrew Grammar* (Andover, Mass., 1821). Photo: David Partington. Widener Library: 2266.20.

Page 181. The Francis A. Countway Library of Medicine. Photo: Louis Reens.

Page 183. Title page of Hebrew Bible (Amsterdam, 1635). Houghton Library: X 16.69*.

Page 185. Widener Library shelflist volume (U.S. class). Widener Library.

Page 187. The *Harvard Crimson*, 6 October 1966.

Page 188, *above*. The Radcliffe Library in the 1890s. Radcliffe College Archives.

Page 188, *below*. The Hilles Library.

Page 191. A microfiche from the Distributable Union Catalog.

Page 193. D. Neubauer, comp., *Catalogue of the Hebrew Manuscripts in the Jews' College* (Oxford, 1886).

Page 194. Israeli election posters preserved in microform by the Judaica Department.

Page 201. The Harvard Depository. Harvard Planning Group.

Page 203. The Monroe C. Gutman Library of the Graduate School of Education.

Page 205. A page of a manuscript of Hegel's Geisteslehre als Einleitung in die Philosophie and a printout describing the Hegel collection. Photo: William Mercer.

Page 207. A view of the roof over Widener Library. Photo: William Mercer.

Index

213

215